D1180212

IDEAS IN CONFLICT

IDEAS IN

# CONFLICT

*Theodore J. Gordon*

ST. MARTIN'S PRESS

ST. MARTIN'S PRESS INC.
175 Fifth Avenue New York NY 10010

MACMILLAN AND COMPANY LIMITED
Little Essex Street London WC2
also Bombay Calcutta Madras Melbourne

THE MACMILLAN COMPANY OF CANADA LIMITED
70 Bond Street Toronto 2

*to* Ann, *who believes in Santa Claus and people*

# PREFACE

It is the purpose of this book to examine some contemporary
outcast ideas, some proposed concepts that have been considered and rejected as false by prominent and articulate
spokesmen of our time. It is my hope in this examination not
only to open some of these ideas for reconsideration, but to
examine the process by which these kinds of ideas are rejected in our society.

In most of the case histories that form the basis of this
book there is an element of emotion associated with rejection. Sometimes the emotion is absolute rage and the rejection
assumes proportions of suppression. Sometimes the emotion
is a bored, condescending, barely detectable no, but a no
just as effective as rage.

The ideas have several features in common. First, they have all been rejected; that is, they are not generally accepted by our scientific community. Second, these hypotheses could be very important to us if eventually shown to be true. They tell of such things as the potential fiery end of the world; of communication between minds, of the search for the origin of life.

I believe the ideas discussed in this book may be true, if not completely and in the form presented, then at least in some allied mode. Some are unlikely, but none are impossible.

Most of these hypotheses have a principal proponent, a champion, who firmly believes in his ideas, who is willing to stand before his peers and say, "This is my idea, world. It is true." These men are the true heroes of this book. It is only through people like them that we have made any progress at all.

# ACKNOWLEDGMENTS

Many people who were sympathetic to the basic idea of this book and provided information and encouragement to me knew they might later be embarrassed by the publication of what they told me. Yet they helped and without them I could not have written this book. One such person wrote me:

> In retrospect, thinking back over what you've written, I'm not at all sure that its publication will do my reputation any good at all; indeed, it will probably stir up more controversy and annoy hell out of some of the people you mention (and some you don't mention). I suppose that I've grown fairly immune to such things by now, though; and even if publication of this chapter won't help me at all (and might even hurt

some, who knows?), perhaps it will do a service of some kind
if it aids even in a small way to help some other scientist in
the future. My own feeling is, frankly, that the narrow-
minded types who dominate science are not likely to read
your book, nor be swayed by it (or any book like it) if they
did happen to read it. But since we all have to make the attempt to broaden our fellow man's perspectives . . . I can
hardly ask you to do more than be as accurate as you
can . . .

I hope, gentlemen, I have been accurate and your trust was
not misplaced.

# CONTENTS

IDEAS IN CONFLICT

# (1

# THE
# JUDGES

There are new and vital ideas in the air; there are new concepts in the making. Ours is the age of innovation. Our expanding economy feeds on innovation, devouring new ideas, transforming them into the seeds of national security or consumer comforts. Change is the norm. We need fast and brilliant discoveries to solve the dilemmas of the population explosion. The forces we command have begun to match those of nature, yet we need more innovation, used effectively and quickly or we will perish.

The mere use of some of our creations demands further invention. As we deplete our resources we must discover synthetic substitutes. As we develop automation, we must create a human theory of leisure and abundance. As we invent weapons we must invent their antidote to preserve status quo. As our anxiety grows we must invent a whole science of behavior.

New ideas descend on us, the public, in a cacophony of genius. We are probing the processes of life and heredity, reaching an understanding of the gene. We are experimenting with government and economic motivation in the Great Society. In the deepening and expanding disciplines of the behavioral sciences we are trying to find out why men act as they do. We are seeking the causes of war, yet at the same time inventing new weapons. The same beam of light that can cut metals is being used to probe the brain. We are going to the moon, and Mars. That which seems at first so improbable or implausible is tomorrow's reality.

Most newly proposed ideas push the existing state-of-the-art along well-established lines, expanding old fields, extending old technologies out from a body of knowledge and experience built over many years by many people. But occasionally there comes an idea which is a discontinuity in this orderly evolution of thought, an unanticipated step which makes man progress in a new direction or with unexpected rapidity. Such an idea is a mutation. If the mutation is beneficial, it can boost man a notch higher into civilization, and help him preserve and develop his emerging species.

Certainly we have many examples of this type of unforeseen contribution. The invention of the telescope, the sudden emergence of the laser, some implications of the theory of relativity, X rays, radioactivity, quantum mechanics, Newtonian mechanics, Copernican astronomy; all of these were new ideas thrust boldly forward with few preliminaries. These were mutant thoughts which took us years ahead in single brilliant steps.

This new kind of idea is often greeted by a burning at the

stake. We tend to reject the unfamiliar. For all our need to be creative, for all the reasons to progress, for all our vaunted achievements and publicized open-mindedness, radically new ideas find few supporters. Some of the ideas which are now clearly the very jewels of our existence were absolutely and finally rejected by prominent spokesmen of their age. Ideas which did not coincide with the preconceived mainstream of scientific, political, or religious thought were fought with militant and abusive dedication. Examples of this kind of anti-intellectualism are well known, and even a simple index would fill a book many times the size of this volume. For example, Ignaz Semmelweis, the first man to grasp the significance and importance of asepsis, died mad in 1865, proclaiming that the unclean hands and instruments of doctors carried disease. He forced cleanliness in his hospitals. He had his students and nurses wash their hands after dissecting corpses and treating the festering wounds of other patients. He proved beyond a doubt that puerperal fever deaths after childbirth were drastically reduced with such procedures. He delivered papers, he taught, he cried, he pleaded. Eventually he lost his mind. He had the proof, he saw his patients live while others died, yet only a few believed him. The epidemic theory of the day excluded new ideas; he could not change that dogma.

At the beginning of the nineteenth century, man faced indescribable pain during a surgical operation, and then had only the barest chance of survival. With no anaesthetics available, surgeons had to cut into living, awake flesh. They had to saw through bones of patients who could see and feel the knife. Was there ever a greater incentive for innovation? Yet when Dr. Horace Wells, a Boston dentist, found that nitrous oxide would give the world blessed freedom from pain, he met laughter and derision. He arranged for a demonstration of his discovery in the most famous hospital in the East. He knew it would work; he had anesthetized himself and others many times. That day, the day he tried to show the world, it didn't work.

He was introduced to the incredulous gallery as an inventor of anesthesia *(snickers)*. He was introduced as a man who had discovered a method of eliminating the natural pain of a surgical operation *(giggles)*. He could, said his sponsor, make the patient fall into a deep sleep while the surgeon worked on an arm or the stomach or brain *(laughter)*. A volunteer from the audience, please. *(Good old Tom, fat, good fellow needs a tooth pulled.)*

"Breathe deeply," says Wells. *(My God, old Tom is out. Could this be real?)*

"Ouch," says Tom *(explosive laughter)*. "Humbug."

Wells didn't know a heavy person required a larger dosage of the gas. The time for anesthesia had not yet come.

Socrates, Galileo, Servetus, Maxwell, Mendell, Ampère, Heaviside, Pasteur, Helmholtz, Planck, Röntgen, Lister, all of these and others faced the *establishment*. They proposed the unusual, the mutant idea. They were at first rejected.

But who makes up the establishment that can pass judgment for us? There are three groups in our society that have the awesome task of deciding what is good and true and what is evil and false. These are: the scientific community, the Church and the government. Often new ideas must pass the scrutiny of all three before they are accepted. Each group has its own leaders, its own vested interests, its own motivations, its own ends which predictably and inevitably color its objectivity.

We have seen this pattern repeated—from the concept of the ether to the absolutism of the speed of light; from animism to the Holy Ghost; from the Divine Right of Kings to the metaphysical Marx. But, to many, *science* is gradually eroding the transcendental absolutes which were once the cornerstones of religion; for example, divine creation vs. Darwinism, or geocentricism vs. the Copernican system. And government has assumed the function of legislating moral values. To science are now relegated the understanding, prediction, and control of nature and to government the definition of good and evil and the punishment of wrongdoing. So religion is left with the *why* of life and the metaphysical understanding of existence, the cause for being.

Three domains of knowledge and existence then emerge, three pockets of overlapping and almost invulnerable power. Each compartment may influence the others, as, for example, the discovery of refined techniques for human motivation will certainly affect governmental structure and control. But at any point in time the three sit as judges, passing on the puny ideas presented to them. When the new ideas reinforce that which is known and accepted as good and true they are admitted, since the power of the judge is thereby enhanced. If the new idea is contradictory to the knowledge on which the power of the judges is based, it is in trouble and the innovator may be burned at a figurative stake.

There is a hierarchy between these judges. In the 2000 years since Christ, religion has been supreme for perhaps two-thirds of the time, molding governments and usually subjugating science to its dogma. Government has recently emerged as the leader, moving both science and religion to its ends. The time of science is yet to come.

Of the three groups, only the scientists have attempted to introduce a logical and codified reception system by which newly proposed data can be rationally examined before being accepted as "truth." This is the "scientific method" which purports to open its arms to all new ideas to give them a fair test in open publication and review. The method implies that there are no cliques in science, that an idea will stand on its own worth, not on the opinion of pre-eminent scientists. Presumably the stature of the proponents or proposers of the hypothesis does not influence its treatment or eventual success. Yet this rational, democratic, idealistic approach has failed repeatedly, perhaps because scientists are people who, even as you or I, are impressed by titles, rank, glory, and can suffer the ego-starving jealousies which may accompany not-invented-hereness.

The scientific method succeeds most of the time. It begins with careful observation, with analytic studies and measurement of phenomena. Since the business of science is basically one of prediction and understanding of nature, the scientist will generalize from his observation to form a synthetic hypothesis, an educated guess about what's going on. He tests this guess in every way possible, molding it until it can stand by itself as a productive tool. Publication usually follows to establish priority and in theory to permit other scientists to duplicate the experiments, or use them as a basis for their own work.

Yet the method fails. In 1960 several thousand infants were born deformed as a result of the drug Thalidomide. It had first been synthesized as a new sedative in Switzerland in 1954. Tested on laboratory animals, it seemed to produce no effects. The West German firm, Chemie Grünenthal, continued the development of the drug. They found that for people it worked as a hypnotic agent giving deep, all-night sleep. It was marketed in West Germany as Contergan, prescription not required. It seemed ideal; there seemed to be no side effects, and large overdosages did not cause death. It was compounded with other medicines for complaints ranging from colds to the nausea of pregnancy. Its use spread quickly from Germany to England to Australia. An application had been filed with the Food and Drug Administration for permission to sell the drug in this country. Two months later the connection between taking the drug during pregnancy and the deformity of the infants was deduced. Dr. Widukind Lenz of Hamburg found the relationship after sending out questionnaires to parents of deformed infants and their physicians. Circumstantial evidence collected from these answers and similar studies elsewhere in the world convicted the drug. On November 20, 1961, Lenz delivered a paper at a pediatric meeting stating his suspicion of a specific drug and that he had warned the manufacturer. Six days later Grünenthal withdrew the drug.

While the method has succeeded far more often than it has failed, its many failures have been spectacular. For example: Mesmer's discovery of hypnotism was denounced by a panel of scientists appointed by the French government. Galileo contradicted Aristotelian mechanics and had to resign his post at the University of Pisa; his experience at the Inquisition as a result of his defense of the Copernican system is well known. Freud's first writings were received with hostility from orthodox clinical psychologists. The ideas of Copernicus were challenged for a century and a half. Leibnitz, inventor of the calculus, was brought before an international conference of scholars to prove his priority over that of Newton's. When Lister presented his findings to the British Medical Association he was met with ridicule and intellectual inertia. Pasteur was fought and satirized, most scientists believing that the microbes he discovered were the result of fermentation and putrefaction, rather than their cause.

The significant aspect of this list is that these are only

a few of the thoughts which were once proposed to the scientific community, rejected and later accepted for use in our knowledge bank. How many other mutant ideas were rejected inappropriately and are unused today because of our lack of insight?

The scientists have the real problem of distinguishing the crank from the contributor. Dr. Laurence J. Lafleur, writing in *The Scientific Monthly*, said:

> . . . Any widely known scientist . . . receives a considerable stream of letters that he classifies as "crank" letters, which propose, and dogmatically affirm to be true, propositions which the scientist recognizes as preposterous, ridiculous, and contrary to all the recognized truths of his science. . . . But here we may interpose an objection. Is not the scientist, in rejecting the crank letter, and even in labeling it "crank" just as dogmatic as the man whose theory he rejects?

Dr. Lafleur goes on to propose a series of tests that will permit the scientist to distinguish between the crank and the real contributor. His tests are tough. To paraphrase them:

(1) Does the innovator know what theories he proposes to supersede?

(2) Is there an adequate reason for making a change, at least of weight equal to evidence for the existing theory?

(3) Does the proposer have sufficient evidence to challenge an established body of knowledge?

(4) Does the new hypothesis offer an adequate substitute for superseded ideas?

(5) Does the proposed hypothesis fit all fields?

(6) Is the new theory capable of mathematical accuracy to a degree at least equal to the old theory?

(7) Does the proposer show a disposition to accept minority opinion?

Presumably, if an innovator can answer all of these properly, he is authentic. I suspect that there aren't many valid mutant ideas which could pass this code of acceptability. Certainly most of the examples referred to earlier would have been rejected.

It is only fair to point out that most new ideas are not rejected without consideration. Most rejected ideas are scrapped because they are simply wrong. Nevertheless, our best inquisitive syllogistic methods have permitted some good ideas to slip by, because judges are human.

The role of the Church as a protector of the integrity of our precious bubble of knowledge has, of course, diminished greatly since the Inquisition, but has not completely stopped. As a matter of fact the reviewing of potentially heretical literature by the Congregation of the Holy Office represents a present-day continuation of the Inquisition.

Some estimates place the total number of people executed by the Spanish Inquisition as high as thirty thousand. These people died for the crime of opposing dogma, or at least of being accused of opposing dogma. The Inquisition, of course, had very wide influence on thought and expression. Had he not recanted, Galileo would have been murdered by the Church for writing that the earth rotated around the sun rather than the sun around the earth as any religious person of the time knew to be true.

Galileo, brought to his knees before the ecclesiastic court, was offered the choice of recantation or burning. Pope Paul V had, after all, warned him years before that he was flirting with heretical ideas.

For speculating on the nature of matter, the universe, and its relationship to man, the Italian philosopher Giordano Bruno was persecuted by the Inquisition. As Tyndall put it, he reached "the sublime generalization that fixed stars are suns, scattered numberless through space and accompanied by satellites, which bear the same relation to them as the earth does to our sun or our moon to our earth." Bruno was accused of heresy and was pursued through Switzerland, France, England, and Germany. Finally in 1592 he was captured in Venice and imprisoned for years, degraded, excommunicated, and turned over to the civil authorities with the request that "he be treated gently and without the shedding of blood." This was the instruction for burning and he was burned at the stake on February 16, 1600.

Michael Servetus, the Spanish scholar who first described the pulmonary system, opposed the Holy Trinity and was burned at the stake as a heretic in 1553.

The religious judge has been far less lenient than the scientific.

When Darwin advanced his ideas on evolution the reaction of the Church was severe and predictable, but the time of the Inquisition had passed. Evolution, poorly understood, was, and is yet, attacked as blasphemy and heresy. "Man evolved from ape? Can this be the divine plan?"

Science is today working in directions which some may consider antireligious. New discoveries may have even greater impact on religion than the popularization of evolutionary theory. Three of the most significant new ideas that could be challenged by religious dogma are: the discovery of alien life forms, the creation of primitive life in the laboratory, and the practical attainment of immortality. How will organized religion greet these achievements?

In 1945, in the United States an argument was raging in government and scientific circles. The same argument was taking place in Russia at about the same time. We derived one answer and they the other. The different approaches which we decided upon account, in large measure, for Russia's early pre-eminence in space and for the much heralded "missile gap." The question was this: Should we (fill in U.S. or U.S.S.R.) develop a ballistic missile delivery system? We have the atomic bomb. Can we deliver it using a missile?

At the time of the argument, the bomb was so large that it wasn't clear that a missile could be constructed to deliver it. Dr. Vannevar Bush who had made magnificent contributions to education and electrical engineering, was, at the time, chairman of the Research and Development Board of the Army and Navy. During the war, of course, he had had over-all responsibility for the development of radar and the atomic bomb. Now in 1945 he had to recommend on the future delivery system. Here is part of his testimony to a Senate Committee:

> There has been a great deal said about a 3000-mile high angle rocket. In my opinion such a thing is impossible for many years. The people who have been writing these things that annoy me have been talking about a 3000-mile high angle rocket shot from one continent to another, carrying an atomic bomb and so directed as to be a precise weapon which would land exactly on a certain target, such as a city. I say, technically, I don't think anyone in the world knows how to do such a thing, and I feel confident that it will not be done for a very long period of time to come . . .

The Russians, on the other hand, went ahead to build a large rocket that could carry their atomic bomb. We waited until thermonuclear bombs were available, or at least shown feasible. This smaller bomb, with its increased output, reduced the size of the required delivery rocket. The lead time of the Russians gave them not only a clear military advantage, it also gave them the impulse they required to get a political jump into space.

It is easy, in retrospect, to pontificate on the error of this decision. I mention it here only to illustrate a case where the judgment of the feasibility of a new idea was made by government, aided by its professional scientists. They judged and they were wrong. We ask in this book: Can we invent a means of presentation, review and judgment that will permit us to make the proper decision next time?

Sometimes scientific truths are matters of national policy. Dr. Trofim Lysenko, the Russian geneticist, legislated against Mendelian genetics when he was a member of the Supreme Soviet. He was influential in prohibiting the teaching of "non-Russian" genetic concepts in Soviet universities and the experimentation with these concepts in government-controlled laboratories. He believed and required adherence to a nineteenth-century doctrine which stated that environmentally developed characteristics could be inherited. This concept was, of course, a great comfort to the Communists, since it implied that human characteristics associated with political beliefs of one generation could be inherited by succeeding generations. Lysenko and his theories have come and gone with the Russian leaders. He lost status after Stalin's death but regained favor under Khrushchev. In 1965, under Kosygin, he was forced to resign as Director of the Soviet Institute of Genetics. Politicians and scientists who link their theories to politics must expect to be out of work occasionally.

Governments set scientific goals. The United States, for example, is going to the moon, a scientific and worthy goal to be sure, but to a large degree, politically motivated. The Harris Survey of the American public showed the Apollo program had only marginal popular support. If it were not for Russian achievements in space, this halfhearted endorsement would change to opposition. Scientists and engineers, as a group, apparently do not support the program either. The journal *Industrial Research* sent questionnaires to, and conducted interviews with, its readers. They found as many supported the program as opposed it, but the largest majority (65%) simply didn't care. The government, however, is ultimately responsible for articulating our goals and implementing the programs by which these are achieved.

Inventions often challenge governments to adapt new modes of operation. An invention is reality and national policy must often be tailored to recognize the *fait accompli*. The hydrogen bomb is here; it is real and no legislation can remove it. Politics have moved into the hydrogen era; there was no alternative. Automation is almost here; politics of abundance are coming. The day after tomorrow we will have the politics of space.

More often, however, it is government which controls innovation. In a wartime environment this control is directed toward national security; in peace, largely toward internal or international political advantage. Over the past fifteen years our government has been responsible for an increasingly large percentage of the research accomplished in the United States. In 1962, for example, its $2,000,000,000 accounted for 65% of all U.S. research and development in the country.

Our government is not only paying for, but is also conducting and guiding, a major portion of the scientific effort being accomplished in this country today.

The National Science Foundation was established in 1950 as a separate federal agency to foster scientific progress in the U.S. by disbursing congressionally authorized research funds to projects of its choice. The foundation spent over

$350,000,000 in 1964, contracting for research in the Antarctic, for deep earth-crust borings, and for weather modification studies. The National Aeronautics and Space Council, the Atomic Energy Commission, the Department of Defense, the armed services, the NASA, the Office of Science and Technology; all of these agencies conduct and contract for research and development in support of their authorized missions.

The Federal government is directing the growth of our knowledge bubble to generate ideas that can be important to us militarily, economically, or politically in our competition with the U.S.S.R. Sometimes these projects conflict with pure scientific interests. The American Institute for the Advancement of Science at its December 1964 meeting criticized two government-sponsored programs: Project Starfish, a high-altitude nuclear explosion over the Pacific, and Project West Ford, the orbiting of millions of tiny copper needles as a military communications reflector. Using the planet as a laboratory, they said, will bring powerful tools into use without understanding their effect. This is not a new criticism. Their worry was: Could these projects somehow affect our weather by reflecting part of the sun's radiant energy, or could they affect our radio telescope experiments or our optical astronomical observations by clouding our seeing? The scientific community was divided.

The government, after all, wants value delivered for its research dollar. This demand creates a whole host of problems for the scientists. They must administrate large budgets and innovate on schedule, skills not necessarily conjugate with scientific imagination. Furthermore, they must, if they work on government projects, pursue those projects for which they are being paid, not those of personal interest.

Thus the Moibus loop is closed: government leads and is led by science. Science sometimes follows a religiously dogmatic model rather than the highly advertised rationalistic methodology. Religion, which once excluded scientific challenges with deadly efficiency, is now challenged itself by the inexorable and inevitable accomplishments of science. Governments have assumed the *morality* function of religion and science; science the *control of nature* function of religion, leaving religion to seek to understand why we are here. The miracles of science and dilemmas of government reinforce this religious role.

The public at large cannot be the judge of the importance and relevance of new ideas. People want to believe the bizarre. Men believe in certain fairy tales. They want to believe in mysticism. They want to be scared a little. The gullibility of the public has been demonstrated in many ways, many times. Charlatanism and fraud are easy to perpetuate.

Witchcraft and demonology, superstition, electronic cures were accepted by the public; yet the telephone, the airplane, the automobile, and the tin can, to name a few, were all rejected initially. The public is no judge.

There stands the dilemma. Who is there to judge the merits of mutant ideas if it is not the constituted authorities of Religion, Government, or Science and not the anarchy of public opinion? The answer has been: The experts of tomorrow, who in retrospect can see which new ideas prove themselves and earn the right to a respected place in man's body of knowledge. When an idea of today fights the tide of preconceived opinion and is rejected with absolute finality, it is in good company. For such was the treatment given the most revered fundamentals of our own science. Let tomorrow be the judge.

# ( 2

# THE
# MIRACLES
# OF
# EXODUS

In 1950 an unknown scholar published a theory about the formation and nature of our solar system. The scientist was neither an astronomer nor a physicist. He was a psychiatrist, and a student of ancient works; an unlikely background for the formation of a revolutionary cosmological theory. His premise was that the ancient writings of the people of the earth described real events and should be believed for what they say, not for what we think they say. The world which emerges from these stories is almost incredible and cannot be explained in terms of an orderly Copernican universe. They describe a chaotic universe, a changing universe, a universe of a wrathful God, a universe in contradiction to the established scientific model. Around these ancient writings this scholar constructed a cosmological theory. It stated that in times not long past, the earth survived catastrophes, flood, fire, earthquake, almost complete loss of human life on earth, as a result of the near collision of bodies in our solar system. The author of these ideas received ridicule and abuse; his ideas were labeled ridiculous, preposterous, obviously false. Scientific pressure groups were formed to suppress publication of the theory. Yet some important features of the hypothesis have been quietly confirmed in the years since the theory was first stated. Somehow, self-consciously, arguments about the validity of the theory and the author's right to articulate it are still continuing after fifteen years.

The Bible described many miracles such as the escape of the Israelites from Egypt, crossing through the sea opened by the east wind.

> . . . the Lord caused the sea to go back by a strong east wind all that night, and made the sea dry land, and the waters were divided.
> And the children of Israel went into the midst of the sea upon the dry ground and the waters were a wall unto them on their right hand, and on their left.
>
> (Exodus 14:21 and 22)

Many wise men have argued about the nature of this passage. Did those ancient historians mean literally that the sea opened to allow the Israelites to pass or was the story an allegory, the parting of the sea representing the dawning of a new age?

If one were to search mythology, the ancient writings, the sacred books, the tales of the remote past of other races and nations, he would find other stories which describe roughly the same event. Dr. Immanuel Velikovsky, who conducted such a search, tells of an old Chinese story that marks the beginning of Chinese history, describing a world in flames and the waters overtopping, ". . . the great heights, threatening the heavens with their floods." He found an ancient Peruvian tale of a time when ". . . the ocean left the shore and with a terrible din broke over the continent; the entire surface of the earth was changed in this catastrophe." The Choctaw Indians of Oklahoma said the earth was dark for a long time but when the light reappeared "it was mountain-high waves rapidly coming nearer."

The Conquistadores in Yucatán found that the Mexican Indians remembered a story about their ancestors who had escaped their enemies when a path was cleared for them through the middle of the sea. This tale was so similar to that of the Biblical exodus, the early missionaries believed the Indians to be descendants of Moses.

A Lapland god is supposed to have said, ". . . I shall cause the sea to gather together itself up into a huge towering wall which I shall hurl upon your wicked earth children." Compare this to Exodus 15:8 ". . . the waters were gathered together, the floods stood upright as a heap . . ."

There are other examples as well, of races of the world remembering the splitting seas, the waters racing down on the land, drowning all in their path. Is this part of what psychologist Carl Jung calls the collective unconscious? Jung felt that the minds of men were predisposed to think in certain patterns and these patterns evolved well-defined tales, or archetypes, which were buried deep in the subconscious, but came to the surface as similar folk tales or similar beliefs in isolated races. Certainly the splitting of the sea would qualify as a Jungian archetype, because in almost every area where man's memories were recorded, man remembered roughly the same event. There could be another explanation; it could have happened.

Other calamities described in the Biblical tale of Exodus are also remembered collectively. What some races remember as the sun standing still, others on the opposite side of the world remember as a prolonged night. There are world-wide stories of massive earthquakes and floods, rivers turning to blood, fire and hot stones hailing down from the sky, days of darkness, hurricanes that blew for days and nights. Even the Biblical tale of manna, that ambrosia which dropped from heaven to feed the Israelites wandering in the dark desert, is found in the legends of other races of the world.

Mexican folklore contains this story: ". . . There came a rain of fire; all that existed was burned and a rain composed of sandstone fell . . . then the red mountains also lifted themselves up . . . the sun consumed itself (was darkened); all houses were destroyed and all the lords or chiefs perished." The translation continues, describing the catastrophe.

> Then . . . the waters became swollen by the mere will of the Heart of Heaven and there came a great inundation from above and descended upon the people . . . they were deluged and then a thick resinous substance fell from the sky. The face of the earth was obscured and a dark rain commenced and fell during the day and during the night . . . there was the great sound of fire overhead. The people ran pushing each other and filled with despair . . . they endeavored to mount upon the houses and these, falling in, threw them to earth again. They wished to climb trees, but these swayed and cast the people from them; they tried to enter caves, but these shut themselves before them . . .

Was this a simple earthquake that the old Mexican sages were describing or was it a world calamity which was also described in the Bible, in Chinese folklore, in Peru; in fact, almost everywhere that memories exist?

Are all of these stories simply archetypes, quirks of the way the mind works? Or are these descriptions of isolated local catastrophes that so impressed the minds of the primitive people of the world? Perhaps, just perhaps, these stories describe a single event, a world cataclysm remembered as the miracles of Exodus. If they do, what could have happened in that terrible instant of time, 3500 years ago?

In 1950, Dr. Immanuel Velikovsky published a most unusual book, *Worlds in Collision,* which holds that these stories do coincide in time and do describe a world-wide calamity of proportions so overpowering and severe that they are hard to imagine today. Furthermore, the stories describe not one, but a series of catastrophes, before and since the time of Exodus. Dr. Velikovsky arrives at this position through a most scholarly and meticulous search of very ancient writings, archaeology, paleontology, and astronomy.

What could have caused such unearthly horror? His thesis was that, over the centuries past, the earth had encountered other heavenly bodies which, because of their close approach, caused earthquakes and floods, slowing of the earth's rotation or wide shifting of its axis. He believes that the story of Exodus and the other folklore generated at about the same time tell of such a near miss. This time, the body that endangered the earth was a comet, a protoplanet that originated from an eruption on the planet Jupiter. The comet, which had traveled for centuries on a highly elliptic orbit, twice passed near the earth, causing great calamity. Its trailing tail enveloped the earth and gave rise to forty years of obscurity. Since the comet's atmosphere was rich in hydrocarbons, great flaming seas of burning petroleum rained down on the earth. A form of the hydrocarbons (carbohydrates or proteins) was the sweet manna which the Israelites and other nations gathered for subsistence while they were without other food after the encounter.

The comet periodically approached Mars, and Mars, in its shifted orbit, also caused destruction on the earth in a later near collision (687 B.C.). The comet then settled into its present circular orbit around the sun and became the planet Venus.

Dr. Velikovsky envisioned certain physical conditions which were, to say the least, contrary to scientific belief. He stated, among other ideas, that the sun, the planets, and the comets were electrically charged; that the planets have been in their present orbits for only a few thousand years; that extended magnetic fields permeated the solar system; that the surface temperature of Venus must be very hot since some of its motion had recently changed to heat through its close encounter with the earth; that its atmosphere must be rich in hydrocarbons and that some of these hydrocarbons rained on the earth during the encounter; that comets result from planetary eruptions; that Mars is a dead planet and its orbit has changed significantly; and that Jupiter emits radio noise (stated in a later [1953] paper). *Worlds in Collision* and Velikovsky's later books contain many more claims touching the disciplines of geology, paleontology, cosmology, celestial mechanics, and archaeology.

No wonder the publication of Velikovsky's book was greeted by skepticism and, in some cases, outright hostility. *The New York Times,* for example, said in its review, "Were it not that it took years to compile and collate hundreds of citations and footnotes, a critical reader might well wonder if this quasi-erudite outpouring is not an elaborate hoax designed to fool scientists and historians." Others cried fraud.

Many scientists took to their typewriters to criticize. They presented papers. They belittled and discredited. There were very few who argued objectively or argued to let him be heard. What had he done? Velikovsky had formulated a cosmological theory opposing most notions of the day by piecing together memories, snatches of folklore recorded in dusty archives, the tales of mankind; he fitted these to geological and archaeological observations. They all said one thing to him: There have been world catastrophes, the time of Exodus was a time of world cataclysm, that cataclysm may have been caused by the close approach of a comet, and that comet went into orbit around the sun to become the planet Venus.

The reaction of the scientific community to the "impossible" ideas of Velikovsky took four major forms: extreme pressure to stop publication of his book; vociferous and vituperative articles intended to discredit his ideas, some apparently written without even a cursory reading of his text; refusal of space to permit him to attempt to refute his detractors; and finally, the serious, frightening proposal that scientific review boards be established to avoid publication of such nonsense in the future.

My acquaintance with the book *Worlds in Collision* is only recent. Somehow I didn't cross its path in 1950, when it topped *The New York Times'* best-seller list for twenty weeks. During a plane trip to the East several months ago, my companion, an erudite engineer, recalled fragments of this remarkable story. It occupied our attention from Los Angeles to Cape Kennedy. Several weeks later I borrowed his old copy of the book. When I completed reading this remarkable story, it occurred to me that now, sixteen years after its writing, some scientific corroboration or refutation of the ideas presented might have been uncovered. I wrote to Dr. Velikovsky in care of Macmillan Company, publishers of the volume which I had borrowed, to ask if such data were now available. The answer seemed to be a long time in coming; I thought perhaps the publishers had lost track of Velikovsky. I was mistaken. Macmillan hadn't lost track of Velikovsky, Velikovsky had lost Macmillan many years before.

When I received his answer, he wrote ". . . From the fact that you have mailed your letter to the care of Macmillan . . . I learn that you are not fully aware of the fate of my first book—the reaction it provoked, the demand made by some places of learning to discontinue its publication, and the resultant transfer of the publication rights to Doubleday. . . ."

Dr. Velikovsky was right, I certainly was unaware of the furor. With the help of some sources he suggested, and some references I discovered, I tracked back over the years and learned about lack of reason in our age of reason, lack of understanding in this day of truth. The truth or falsity of all or part of Dr. Velikovsky's ideas is certainly a question for debate; the right for him to express his ideas should never have been questioned.

When the book was published by Macmillan, it was a success by any standard. Some of its conclusions had been carried in the popular press, and the reaction which these pre-publication articles drew stimulated initial sales of the book. Macmillan had a best-seller. Yet Macmillan, with Velikovsky's approval, transferred rights to the book to Doubleday on June 8, 1950, when sales were at their peak. Why? Leonard Lyons, in his column of June 15, said:

> . . . A publishing official admitted, privately, that a flood of protests from educators and others had hit the company in its vulnerable underbelly—the textbook division. Follow-

ing some stormy sessions by the board of directors, Macmillan reluctantly succumbed, surrendered its rights to the biggest money-maker on its list.

Velikovsky was told that professors had been refusing to see Macmillan salesmen. Some refused to publish with them unless the publishing house disassociated itself from Velikovsky. Dr. Laurence J. Lafleur, then associate professor of philosophy at Florida State University, defended this attitude as reasonable and just. He said:

> . . . the success of scientific books will depend in large measure on the reputation of the publisher . . . most instructors will peruse the table of contents to see whether the approach and subject matter are suitable, and will read a few sections to check on readability and general soundness, but will rely on the reputation of the author or publisher that the rest of the text will be reasonably sound. When the name of a publisher no longer serves to guarantee the scientific integrity of the book, the teacher tends to avoid that publisher. The so-called suppression of an unorthodox work is thus explained . . .

Even after the book moved to Doubleday, professional scientists were concerned that just being in the same publishing house would bring shame on them. One scientist, apparently afraid of this contamination, told his publisher, a Doubleday subsidiary, that he would turn the royalties of his book over to charity and would henceforth not revise it as long as Velikovsky was in the same stable.

In Germany, in 1952, after five printings by its first publisher, the book was attacked and publication suspended. Here, apparently, the pressure came from theologians.

In America, even though *Worlds in Collision* had proved to be a best-seller and had stimulated fresh thinking and a

good deal of popular support, Macmillan felt obliged to
fire the editor who had accepted the book and to engage
in discussions about a prepublication scientific review panel
whose job it would be to insure that similar travesties
couldn't be made again.

The story of this theory-censoring board is worth reviewing. This proposal was reported by Mr. Warren Guthrie in
an article in *Science,* a greatly respected scientific journal.
The article dealt with a discussion held at the December
1950 annual meeting in Cleveland of the American Association for the Advancement of Science. The topic of the discussion had been "Books, Civilization, and Science," and on
the panel were representatives from the University of
Chicago and Harvard, newspaper publishers, publishers of
scientific literature, including both books and periodicals.
The article states:

> . . . The publishers frequently print, it was charged, and
> the public likes, the sales records show, the *wrong* kinds of
> scientific books. The best-sellers dealing with matters scien-
> tific are those such as *Worlds in Collision* or *Dianetics.*
> More sound, more responsible, though less sensational works,
> even when written with an eye to the general public as audi-
> ence, are seldom as widely read. It was with this problem
> that our group became largely concerned.
>
> For the charge that they were at fault, the publishers had
> an immediate and effective answer. Most of the books against
> which the scientists were most vocal were not listed by their
> publishers as "scientific." That the public regards them as
> such, say the publishers, is beyond their control. Further-
> more, as Mr. Skelley (Macmillan) pointed out, in at least
> one case in which a book that the panel regarded as un-
> sound enjoyed a wide sale, the publisher voluntarily trans-
> ferred his rights to another company at heavy financial loss.
> Other representatives of the publishing group made clear
> their interest in seeing that books presented on their scien-

tific lists are acceptable to the scientific fraternity, as well as popular with the general public.

Nonetheless, the "wrong" kinds of scientific literature do get published. Feeling there should be some protection to the public from the unsound, and a consequent greater interest in the best scientific writing, the panel offered several constructive suggestions.

First, to assist the publishers in their job of selecting those manuscripts that merit publication, it was suggested that some sort of board of review be created from the ranks of the scientists themselves. This board would be quick to eliminate the spectacular but non-scientific.

The panel recognized, of course, that this sounded like censorship. Therefore, other means of control were sought. One educator felt that the best safeguard was complete reversion to scientific methodology which by its unwritten law requires publication first in scientific journals, prior to popularization. It requires that new ideas

> . . . be submitted to a jury of the writer's peers—to those who by training and experience are most competent to examine and to criticize it . . . No publisher . . . should yield to the temptation of selling a book full of radically new or obviously unorthodox ideas until he has learned of the previous presentation of those ideas to the scrutiny of the author's scientific peers in technical journals or at professional meetings.

The panel did not believe full support of these new ideas was always required, just a "modicum" of support. I wonder if Galileo had a modicum of support? (Let me say parenthetically that I do not believe that most scientists share the reactionary views of this symposium.)

The attackers were very active. Some pro-Velikovsky forces thought that all of this activity and scorn really hid "fear and trembling." A few of the techniques used were:

> The idea is so obviously false, I find it difficult to comment. I haven't read the book and I don't intend to. It is all lies. This must be a hoax.
>
> Velikovsky says . . . (here would follow a misquote). He is obviously wrong because (here would follow an attack on the misquotation).

Apparently many of the people applying pressure had not read the book and were simply following the position established by the scientific hierarchy.

Velikovsky did at least three things to raise this great ire. First, it was generally believed that he had not submitted his work for "review by his peers" according to best scientific tradition; second, his presentation did not move from hypothesis to logical proof using observed data or mathematical analysis to support the arguments; rather, it reported historical data, derived an hypothesis which fit the data, and left the observational checking to other scientists. Third, he presented a theory in direct contradiction to firmly held beliefs of his day, which were not recognized to be in need of repair.

While Velikovsky published his work in a way that attracted a great deal of popular notice, he had had contact with portions of the scientific community prior to publication. Professor H. M. Kallen, then Dean of the New School for Social Research, read the manuscript before publication and felt that Velikovsky

> . . . has built up a serious theory deserving of the careful attention of scholars . . . showing a kind of scientific imagination which on the whole has been unusual in our times. If this theory should prove to be valid, not only astronomy but history and a good many of the anthropological and social

sciences would need to be reconsidered both for their content and explanation. If it should not prove to be valid, it would still be one of those very great guesses which occur far too infrequently in the history of human thought.

This was from correspondence written in 1946 between Professor Kallen and Professor Harlow Shapley, who later became a very outspoken opponent of Velikovsky. This letter contained a request that spectroscopic data on the atmosphere of Venus be obtained to determine if hydrocarbons were present, a critical test of Velikovsky's hypothesis which Velikovsky attempted to make before publication. Professor Shapley answered Professor Kallen, referring Velikovsky to Dr. Walter Adams of Mount Wilson and other astronomers. One answered that he thought the absorption spectrum of Venus indicated large amounts of carbon dioxide were present in the atmosphere rather than gaseous hydrocarbons. Dr. Adams replied:

> . . . The absorption bands of the petroleum gases are in the infrared, far below where photographic plates can be used. It is true that the spectrum of some of the hydrocarbon compounds do occur in the photographic region, but these would necessarily arise from the gases and not from hydrocarbon dust. There is no evidence of the presence of hydrocarbon gas in the atmosphere of Venus.

From the historical evidence of his research, Velikovsky reasoned hydrocarbon gases *must* be present in the atmosphere of Venus; astronomers assured him to the contrary. He decided to publish regardless.

John J. O'Neill, then science editor of the New York *Herald Tribune,* read the manuscript before publication and was greatly impressed. He said so in his column of August 14, 1946: The work was a "challenge to scientists" and a "stupendous panorama of terrestrial and human histories."

Gordon Atwater, who was then director of the Hayden Planetarium, and Curator of Astronomy of the American Museum of Natural History, also recommended publication of the manuscript. He later lost his job because of his favorable support of Velikovsky. In a recent letter to the *American Behavioral Scientist* magazine, Mr. Atwater, reviewing his position said:

> . . . In 1950, I planned to give over a special show in the Hayden Planetarium to his [Velikovsky's] theories for the benefit of the general public as well as educators and scientists generally. It was my belief that educators and scientists were the ones who would profit most from the message I had in mind. I believed then, as I have believed ever since, that had the American Museum of Natural History not forced me to resign and then cancelled the show, we would have, in recognizing Velikovsky, led institutions of the world to a new and higher level of cultural attainment.

In his comment on this letter, the editor of the *American Behavioral Scientist* said:

> . . . [Mr. Atwater] was summarily dismissed from his post on April 1, 1950 . . . Since that time he has been unable to have any of his writings published; in fact, it would appear that the science of astronomy has read him out of its rolls.

Mr. Atwater's dismissal came one day before his favorable review of the book appeared in *This Week* magazine.

Because of threats of boycott and loud, last-minute complaints before publication, the manuscript was submitted by the publisher to an anonymous scientific review board (Velikovsky's peers?). The publisher took this action because of strenuous and threatening letters which had been received from a leading astronomer in which he threatened to "cut off" relations with Macmillan. The three-man panel apparently gave their okay, because the book was published. When the book was finally on the stands, Velikovsky suffered because of the lack of outspoken scientific support and there was only a "modicum" of outspoken open-mindedness.

The second criticism, that Velikovsky devised an hypothesis to fit historical data and published it without mathematical or observational proof, is true. His extraordinary research led him to certain conclusions about the behavior of the solar system. These conclusions had no immediate proof, per se. In a field such as cosmology there are few absolute proofs, since we don't see planets being created every day. As a result, his detractors called his ideas vague and unsupported. Yet his historical reconstruction led to the prediction of certain physical consequences which could be checked observationally. Many of these have been verified, as we will see. "Lucky guesses," say his opponents.

Astronomer Lloyd Motz and physicist V. Bargmann, in a letter to *Science,* December 21, 1962, gave Velikovsky priority in correctly predicting that Venus would be very hot, that Jupiter would be a source of radio noise, and that the earth's magnetic field extended well above the ionosphere. They recommended that his other ideas also be re-examined objectively even though they disagreed with his theories. A letter in the February 15, 1963 issue of *Science* sarcastically derided Motz, Bargmann, and Velikovsky. Poul Anderson said that Swift, in *Gulliver's Travels,* predicted that Mars had two moons: perhaps his ideas should be objectively re-examined. Some science fiction works have been remarkably correct. What about them? He concluded that "While one apple spoils the rest, the accidental presence of one or two good apples does not redeem a spoiled barrelful."

Professor H. H. Hess, Chairman of the Space Board of the National Academy of Science, wrote Velikovsky, ". . . I do not know of any specific prediction you make that has since proven to be false."

The third point was the radical nature of the theory. It simply didn't make sense to most scientists in terms of the generally accepted views of the mechanics of the solar system. Furthermore, there seemed to be little need to change existing theories. The eternal order of the heavens was obvious and satisfying.

Since the clear statement and acceptance of the helio-centric theory of the solar system by Copernicus, as later refined by Newton, Kepler, and others, science has believed that the order of the heavens is almost eternal and unchanging, except for a few unpredictable meteors and comets. Once in motion, mass remains in motion unless acted on by outside forces. The smooth, elliptical paths of the planets are predictable for all time, past and future. In this immutable and pleasing picture, scientific knowledge approximates religious dogma.

In proposing a solar system in which catastrophes were possible, Velikovsky upset astronomers' smooth and orderly system of heliocentric eternity, and supplied religion a natural explanation for the miracle. One favorable reviewer, referring to this absence of interference by the ecclesiastics, said, "After the painful experience with Galileo, the Catholic Church has accumulated more wisdom in scientific epistemology than that revealed by our scientific community."

The man who is responsible for this remarkable furor is not an astronomer or astrophysicist. He is an intense, articulate researcher in ancient writings. He is a scholar, a medical doctor, and a psychiatrist. He lives in a gray stone two-story house, circa 1930, on a quiet street in Princeton, New Jersey, close to the campus, and with some satisfaction watches his theories proven correct one by one. There is a fresh coat of gray paint on the porch floor and his car stands in the driveway, waiting, as he does, as the house does. The brown front door has an antique handle, fastened with a twisted wire. A broom is standing next to it. Mrs. Velikovsky greets you with a firm handshake. No introduction is necessary; she is part of this. In the living room is soft furniture, rounded; the piano has seen use. The rocker is obviously for Dr. Velikovsky, a visitor would do well to save it for him. The French doors at the end of the living room open into the study, full of academic disorder. Physically, he is a big man, who seems bigger through the force of his arguments. Brown suit, worn, bushy white hair that starts late on his forehead, wide-set eyes behind glasses that get pushed up for close inspection of small print, strong accent, strong insistent voice, but with precise grammar; all of these form a man of almost overpowering intensity who believes in his ideas and himself.

He was born in Vitebsk, Russia, seventy years ago. He took his degree in medicine at the University of Moscow. Together with Professor Albert Einstein and Professor Heinrich Loewe, he co-edited *Scripta Universitatis Atque Bibliothecal Hieosolymetanarum* in the years between 1921 and 1924. This intellectual effort was one of the motivating forces behind the formation of the Hebrew University in Jerusalem. Later he studied psychoanalysis in Europe and practiced in Palestine. In 1939, he came to America with his wife and daughters to do library research on the Greek legendary cycle and the Egyptian history of the end of the 18th Dynasty in connection with a planned book on *Freud and*

*His Heroes.* In the course of these studies, Velikovsky came across the coincidental stories contained in various mythologies and this gave rise to a new dating of history and the framing of the catastrophic theme which was later to dominate in his works *Ages in Chaos* and *Worlds in Collision.*

Where are we today with the theories that stirred up such a storm? One of Velikovsky's most telling arguments came out of his study of ancient astronomy. He found that Hindu astronomical records attributed to the year 3100 B.C. (that is, prior to the time of Exodus) omit the planet Venus. The ancient Babylonian astronomers also omitted Venus, but carefully charted other visible planets: Mercury, Saturn, Jupiter, Mars; Venus is missing. The ancient historical records which first report Venus, indicate erratic motion that cannot be accounted for in terms of today's orbital paths. The records are not inaccurate; they were kept with great precision. They were either purposely wrong, or indicative of changing orbits. When Venus is found recorded in later Mexican and Hebrew documents, it is referred to as a star with a tail or a star that smokes.

The Incas called Venus "Chasca," which means "the youth with the long and curling locks," and dedicated altars to the planet. Sacrifices were made to Venus, even to modern times. The old histories of China and Israel talk of the brilliance of the planet, rivaling the sun itself. The planet is called Lucifer, the light bearer, the destroyer.

The comet theory of Venus could explain an old puzzle about the planet. Ancient legends mention the "horns of Venus." We know today that Venus exhibits phases similar to the moon's; i.e., the planet can be seen as a fully illuminated disk or as a partially lit crescent, depending on the relative positions between the planet, the earth, and the sun. It is reasonable to suppose that the phrase "horns of Venus" refers to the crescent phase of illumination. The trouble with this explanation is that the phases of Venus are not visible with the naked eye and, of course, the telescope is a relatively modern device. One can only conclude that at one time Venus appeared in the heavens in quite a different form or that the telescope predates Galileo by a thousand years. This discrepancy has been recognized by some writers since the time of Galileo.

People of ancient Greece, Samoa, and Assyria all apparently knew of the crescent shape of the planet; yet today the crescent shape is clearly beyond the limits of our unaided visibility.

When Velikovsky published *Worlds in Collision* in 1950, astronomers believed the surface temperature of Venus was between $-4°$ F. and $140°$ F. He predicted it must be much hotter because of its recent cosmic encounters. The first confirmation of high temperature came in 1956 when radio observations made at the U.S. Naval Research Laboratory indicated surface temperatures above $600°$ F. The space probe Mariner II scanned Venus in December 1962, and its data showed that the planet's surface temperature was even hotter—about $800°$ F. on both the dark and light sides, a temperature one hundred and fifty degrees above the melting point of lead. Recently, Dr. Velikovsky has suggested that the surface temperature of Venus must be dropping slowly because of the planet's recent origin, and that an experimental program should be undertaken to measure the temperature of the cloud layer at every synodic opportunity.

Our earthbound observations of the planet show other peculiarities. The planet is closer to the sun than the earth. It circles the sun in an almost perfectly circular orbit. Its diameter of 7700 miles is slightly less than that of the earth. Its mass is 81% of ours. Its year is 224 days. No observer has ever seen its surface because the planet is continually shrouded in thick, impenetrable clouds which reflect light as efficiently as new-fallen snow.

Radioastronomy studies of the planet have shown that Venus rotates on its axis in a direction opposite to the direction of its rotation around the sun. Most of the classical cosmological theories of the creation of the solar systems cannot explain this; all rotation should be in the same direction. Astronomers had previously known that several satellites revolved in directions contrary to the general rotation of the solar system, but these were regarded to be bodies captured after the formation of the solar system; does the same reasoning also apply to Venus?

At the April 1966 meeting of the American Geophysical Union, UCLA scientists Drs. P. Goldreich and S. J. Peale presented a paper which stated that the rotation of Venus was somehow linked to the earth. Precise radar observations of the planet have shown that it rotates on its axis once every 243 earth days. With this period, Venus turns the same face toward the earth each time it passes. The scientists said that this resonant orbit was hard to understand unless Venus is very lopsided; probability alone cannot account for it. The moon, of course, always turns the same face toward the earth, rotation once each revolution about the earth. This type of resonant motion resists outside disturbances; once locked, the motion tends to remain locked. When did the earth capture Venus' rotation?

Astronomers refer to a phenomenon known as dicodomy, the appearance of a planet when it is half illuminated by the sun and half in darkness. This phase of lighting is controlled only by the geometrical relationship between the earth, the planet, and the sun. Yet, as precise as our observations are, dicodomy doesn't occur on Venus when expected. This could possibly suggest that the outer reaches of the planet are not spherical.

The presence of hydrocarbons on Venus is crucial to the cosmic reconstruction offered by Velikovsky. In his 1946 correspondence with Dr. Adams and other astronomers, and in *Worlds in Collision,* Velikovsky claims that the atmosphere surrounding Venus must be rich in petroleum (hydrocarbons) and that these compounds will be found in gaseous form as long as Venus is too hot for liquefaction. When his book was published, most astronomers believed that the atmosphere of Venus was composed chiefly of carbon dioxide. In 1955, the famous astronomer Fred Hoyle published a book in which he pictured oceans of oil on the planet and hydrocarbons in the atmosphere, but observational confirmation came in 1962 when the Mariner II data was released. The National Aeronautics and Space Administration announced that the clouds surrounding Venus are over fifteen miles thick and probably are composed of condensed hydrocarbons held in oily suspension.

Sometimes, when our moon is in its crescent phase, the darkened part is faintly visible. This "old moon in the new moon's arms" is attributed to the reflection of earthshine on the surface of the moon. The same sort of phenomenon is seen occasionally on Venus' surface. But Venus is too far away for this faint visibility of the darkened side to be attributed to earthshine. The glow is called the Ashen Light. Perhaps it is a slight phosphorescence or incandescence produced by the planet's heat.

So even though one of our robots has been to Venus, we know very little about the planet. It rotates in the retrograde direction once each 243 days. It is very hot; its surface is obscured by very dense clouds, fifteen miles thick, probably composed of hydrocarbons. Its massive atmosphere may be incandescent or phosphorescent. Observations of the planet have produced anomalies related to the timing of its phases. If earlier reports are to be believed, Venus once had a visible tail.

Now let us look at comets. Almost all folklore associated with comets ascribed to them the task of signaling the end of the world. A nineteenth-century source said, "So lately as in the year 1832, the greatest alarm spread over the continent of Europe, especially in Germany, lest the comet, whose appearance was then foretold by astronomers, should destroy the earth. The danger to our globe was gravely discussed. Many persons refrained from undertaking or concluding any business during that year, in consequence solely of their apprehension that this terrible comet would dash us and our world to atoms." Apparently, this tradition has its roots in antiquity; there appears to have been a fear of comets since earliest history. Perhaps this fear dates back to the time of Exodus.

Most comets move with the solar system and some astronomers now believe some comets originate within our group of planets. There is the barest possibility that some comets come into our system of planets from beyond our solar system, from the deep reaches of space, take one swing around the sun, and depart our solar system on parabolic or hyperbolic orbits never to be seen again. In any event, we know that most comets stay with us, following highly elliptic orbits. While the planets circle the sun in the same direction and lie almost in the same plane, of the comets that travel with us many circle in any direction and lie in any plane. As a comet approaches the sun its tail grows longer and swings in a direction away from the sun. Its brightness exceeds that which could be expected as a result simply of reflectivity; apparently the solar energy excites the comet to some sort of phosphorescence.

Most of the mass of a comet is concentrated in its nucleus. Stretching away from the nucleus and the sun is the tail which may be very large, but is apparently very tenuous. Some comets have grown so large that they have exceeded the diameter of the earth's orbit around the sun. The tail is apparently composed of very minute particles which are pushed away from the nucleus by the solar winds, plasmas which originate on the sun and pervade space.

Comets occasionally pass very close to planets. When this happens, the path of the comet may be grossly affected. We have yet to observe a similar effect on the planet which a comet passes. For example, in 1770, Lexell's comet passed close to the earth. The path of the comet was changed. However, no effect on the earth's motion was noticed. This leads to the conclusion that most comets have very low mass. Thus, their path would be changed by a close approach to a planet, but the path of the planet would not be very much perturbed. The 1770 comet was estimated to weigh less than one ten-thousandth the weight of the earth. Yet no two comets are identical. Some comets are bright, others dim. Some are large, some small. With this kind of variability in trajectory and visible characteristics, is it too unreasonable to presume that once in a great while we may encounter a massive comet? A massive comet passing very close to a planet might affect its rotation, its tides, its year. From Mariner II we know that Venus has almost no magnetic field, yet it is probably an electrical conductor. If it did pass close to the rotating earth, the magnetic lines of force surrounding the earth must have been intersected by the electrically conductive comet-planet, thus producing a considerable charge of electricity. Furthermore, in so doing, a force must have been created which would tend to shift the earth's axis of rotation and slow it down. According to Velikovsky, Venus may have had a stronger magnetic field before its encounter with the earth.

Comets can break apart when they approach the sun. Today we know of no very massive comets; however, it is possible that some large comets have been fragmented near the sun. In 1951, N. T. Bobrovnikoff, Director of the Perkins Observatory, estimated that several comets observed in the nineteenth century came from a single body which probably equaled the mass of the moon. While this would be less than the mass of Venus, it indicates that massive comets are possible.

Comets have been called "big bags of nothing." This refers to their very low apparent densities. Yet several comets have made very close approaches to the heavy planet Jupiter and have not been split apart by the planet's great gravitational attraction. This indicates that, although the density of the comet may be low, the forces binding it together are strong enough to survive a mighty tug.

Velikovsky's view of the cosmos included electrical charges on the sun and planets and magnetic fields extending into space. When his book was published, science recognized no interplanetary plasmas; today their presence is well established. In an address to the Graduate College Forum at Princeton in October 1953, Dr. Velikovsky predicted that Jupiter would be found to emit radio noises. This possibility was not anticipated because of the cold temperature of the planet. Yet, in the solar system envisioned by Velikovsky, planets had electrical charge, and the motion of the gases on such a massive planet could result in radio emissions. In 1955, Drs. B. F. Burke and K. L. Franklin announced their accidental discovery of Jupiter's radio noise.

In the same Princeton lecture, Velikovsky reasoned that the moon's librations, its rocking movements, might be correlated to the magnetic field of the earth. Our space probes have identified a magnetic "shock wave" around the earth which tails off in a direction away from the sun. The moon's librations may well be connected with its passage through this tail. Velikovsky pictured the tremendous craters on the lunar surface being formed during the cosmic encounters when the surface melted to lava and formed bubbles which burst on cooling. Some of the smaller bubbles might not have burst and these would appear as domes. Such domes have been detected on the lunar surface.

As we conceive the earth rotating endlessly around the sun we feel a sense of the infinite, of timelessness. It is thus, we said; it has been thus; it will always be thus. The idea of a catastrophe is almost inconceivable to us; in a way the eternity of the solar system is at the foundation of all we believe. The eons since creation have eroded the earth to its present state; life itself has evolved and will continue to evolve and from this stems our philosophy, scientific and religious. All is in transition on the stable rock of earth on its stable flight around the sun. Yet the nagging idea of a possible cosmic catastrophe keeps appearing. As recently as August 19, 1965, the Associated Press carried a story about a possible future encounter with the asteroid Icarus. This chunk of rock is in orbit around the sun, but its path carries it quite close to Mercury and the earth at times. On June 15, 1968, the body will pass within four million miles of the earth. However, just a slight change in its path as it passes near Mercury could move it closer to the earth, perhaps even to the point of contact. The news article hinted that some European scientists were actually working toward a determination of the possible impact point so that an evacuation could be accomplished in time.

There have been other discoveries which support Velikovsky's picture of past catastrophes. Oceanographic research has turned up a layer of ash, a foot thick in some places, over a very wide area of the Pacific Ocean floor. Some scientists believe that the same layer underlies all ocean beds. They have assumed that it was deposited in a cometary collision. Other oceanographers have reported that, at about the time of Exodus, the water levels in the oceans suddenly dropped about twenty feet and that the glaciers in the Rockies suddenly increased in size. Sandy beaches, discovered in mid-ocean, indicate possible shifting of the mass of water on our globe. Large amounts of nickel, found in ocean-bottom clay, have suggested to oceanographers the fall of a large number of meteorites.

In his book *Earth in Upheaval,* Velikovsky tells of the physical features of the earth which support the chaotic heavens theory. Tremendous quantities of bones and tusks belonging to animals normally found in temperate zones have been found above the Arctic Circle. Apparently, they were once inhabitants of the area and some natural catastrophe caused their extinction. Many of these animals were voracious herbivores and consumed large quantities of vegetable food now absent from the bleak tundra. Quick-frozen mammoths with flesh, skin, and hair have been found buried in Siberia. They perished so quickly and have been found so well preserved in the cold north, that the contents of their stomachs can be botanically identified. Analysis of this residue shows grasses and plants that do not now grow in northern Siberia. Remains of advanced human Neolithic cultures have been found in Alaska; and as Velikovsky predicted in *Worlds in Collision,* page 329, towns have been found in presently uninhabited areas of Siberia. One way to account for such rapid freezing would be through a change in the axis of rotation of the earth.

Catastrophe is written also by the marine fossils found in high mountain ranges, the history of glacial action in equatorial latitudes, relatively recent and sudden reversal of the earth's magnetic poles, the destroyed civilizations, the submerged forests of trees found throughout the world, and the precipitous lowering of the level of the oceans. Remarkably, where techniques of sufficient accuracy are available, many of these geophysical events can be correlated in time, indicating that repeated and severe world catastrophes have taken place. These dates are further confirmed by rings of very old trees, and the collective memories of the world's people reported in *Worlds in Collision.*

Archaeological investigations of the ancient civilizations of the Near and Middle East led Dr. Claude Schaeffer of Collège de France to conclude that tremendous disasters had hit these cultures, five times between 3000 B.C. and 1000 B.C., destroying cities, empires, and populations on a scale unknown in modern times.

The huge rock monoliths of Stonehenge on the Salisbury Plain in England may offer another clue to the theory of the catastrophe. Professor Gerald S. Hawkins, a young American astronomer, has shown by careful computer computations that the rocks form a solar and lunar observatory, aligning precisely with the summer solstices and lunar excursions, for our current day and month. Therefore, the type of catastrophe Velikovsky describes must have occurred before Stonehenge was built. If Velikovsky is right perhaps Stonehenge may have been the first memorial to the new system of the heavens.

The construction of Stonehenge took place over a period

of perhaps five centuries. Dating of the first of its structures has been accomplished through identification of pottery fragments, bone pins, and flint chippers, and through radio-carbon dating of charcoal found in one of the early marker holes of the observatory. The pottery was correlated to other Neolithic samples which were manufactured between 1900 and 1700 B.C. These dates were confirmed by the pins and chippers. The radio-carbon dating test showed the charcoal had burned in 1850 B.C., give or take several hundred years. The median date of these findings is about 1800 B.C., which predates Velikovsky's cataclysm by 300 years. Yet the dating may be inaccurate; a miss of 300 years out of 3500 would not be unusual. There aren't many structures which, because of their exact alignment with the heavens, *must* postdate the catastrophe. If we knew the history of this structure, the people who built it and their reasons, we might know considerably more about Velikovsky's theme.

Some specific criticisms of Velikovsky's hypothesis remain to be answered. If Venus once was a comet on an eccentric orbit, how can its orbit now be almost perfectly circular? The earth, Venus, and Mars today form a three-body system circling the sun. If Venus, as a protocomet, once ranged as far as Mars in its eccentric orbit, how could it be forced into a nearly circular orbit within the earth's orbit? Energy considerations would not permit this with the known planetary masses. Dr. Laurence J. Lafleur raised this most telling objection. He said:

> According to mechanical principles known since Kepler's time, celestial bodies move in closed orbits, traveling over the same path again and again. Consequently, after the last collision, whatever it was, the two planets involved would be left with intersecting orbits. Various known forces could modify such orbits, but as they would take many millions

of years to produce an appreciable modification, it follows
that there can have been no encounters between major members of the solar system.

The same argument was raised by Howard Margolis, in an
article titled "Velikovsky Rides Again" which appeared in
the April 1964 Bulletin of the Atomic Scientists. He said:

> . . . it appears to be inherently impossible for Mars to col-
> lide with Venus at some point outside the earth's orbit, as
> Velikovsky proposes, with the consequence that Venus is
> knocked into a nearly circular orbit outside the earth's orbit.
> This seems to be the case for the same kind of reason that
> you cannot pour two quarts of water into a one quart jar;
> the world, as far as we can tell, simply isn't built that way.

The only possible answer is that kinetic energy was somehow lost by Venus in the encounter and transferred to Mars
and the earth (which would have changed the length of
its year as claimed by Velikovsky), or that other forces of a
magnitude beyond our knowledge are continually at work
and have circularized the path of the planets (also as claimed
by Velikovsky). While electrostatic forces and high energy
plasmas are now known to pervade the solar system, these
forces do not seem to be large enough to influence a planet's
orbit in a short time.

Velikovsky suggests that the flies of the Biblical plague
might have come from the atmosphere or tail of Venus during its close approach. If this is so, how can it be simultaneously claimed that Venus is hot? The answer offered is
that the surface may be hot, but not necessarily the upper
reaches of the atmosphere. Dr. Homer Newell of NASA, in
announcing the Mariner II data, stated that low order life
could possibly exist in the cooler atmosphere.

The question has been raised: If the world stopped rotating, wouldn't all the people fly off? Velikovsky's answer: The earth may have decelerated slowly, or simply tilted both its astronomical and geographical axis.

When the book was first published there were tremendous arguments raging, in private and in print. Today, the arguments are quieter. Dr. Velikovsky feels that the major form of opposition to the book today is the failure to connect its concepts with recent discoveries, or an occasional attempt to discredit a footnote (with no success, he adds).

There is some indication that the academic doors of scientific inquisitiveness are at last beginning to open. Velikovsky wrote me on February 10, 1965:

> I am leaving on Sunday, February 14 for Kent University and Oberlin College, both in Ohio, with two addresses in each . . . Prof. Lloyd Motz, astronomer, Columbia University and myself (will debate) at Guyot Hall, Princeton University, on Thursday, February 25 . . . on the theme:
>
> "Is Venus a new-comer to the planetary family?" The debate with Prof. Hess (Catastrophes and Earth's History) a few weeks ago fared very well . . . On March 4 I shall address the joint meeting of the Earth and Astronomical Sciences, Carnegie Institute of Technology and the Department of Earth and Planetary Sciences, University of Pittsburgh, as guest of both institutions. On March 15, I shall speak at the Forum of the Brown University, with three opponents: professors of geology, physics, and history of mathematics.
>
> From these few details you may conclude that the large portals of science are slowly but widely opening before the non-conformist of yesterday . . .

Why is man afraid of comets? Maybe because we came close to hitting one once, a large one. Can there ever be complete proof of Velikovsky's central hypothesis? Possibly.

Scientists in this country are contemplating sending a rocket payload to an intercept with a comet. The payload will collect data about the makeup of these strange bodies. We may learn where they come from. We may learn if their physical arrangement permits massive nuclei. We may find physical evidence of near collisions with Mars and Venus when we land on the moon. Someday our space probes may sample the clouds of Venus, and perhaps later, its surface. When these data are fitted together, we may learn more about the miracles of Exodus; we may learn the fate of earth; we may even learn something about ourselves and our reaction to new ideas.

# THE
# LEARNED
# WORM

A planarian is a fresh-water flatworm, an unjointed, invertebrate, funny little worm. Its head is shaped like an arrow and contains two "cross-eyed" eye spots; its body is brown or black and it leaves a slimy trail when it crawls. Under the tutorship of some progressive scientists in our country and abroad, this worm just could be responsible for some major revisions to our most sacred concepts of evolution and learning.

The planarian is a very peculiar creature in the evolutionary scheme of things. First of all, if you were to slice it in half, each hemi-worm would regenerate. In fact, if you cut a planarian into five or six pieces, each would grow into a complete worm, with all organs, indistinguishable from a worm that matured from an egg.

The planarians used in this research reproduce by fission; a worm simply splits in two, and the old head grows a new tail, and the old tail, a head. Other species of the worm, however, are interested in sex, but these are hermaphrodites. They contain both male and female organs, and in mating, cross-fertilize. Each lays cocoons containing some sixteen eggs. Thus these worms, depending on their species, can bear young by laying eggs in a peculiar way, or simply split in half like the Almighty atom and where there was one, now there are two. All of which leads to the enigmatic, slightly mythological possibility of a worm becoming not only its own grandpa, but father, mother, and grandma as well.

These creatures are the most complex animals that can reproduce by fission, yet are the simplest with a central nervous system and bilateral symmetry. Their digestive tract starts with a sucker located in their belly. These worms are carnivores and some species are cannibals.

All of this makes the flatworm a very interesting scientific subject. It has, in fact, wrapped its lovable little slimy body around the lives and work of a small group of dedicated researchers in this country and around the world. The aspect which this group has found most interesting is that the planarian can learn and remember what it has learned. That, in itself, would not be surprising, since the worms do have a sort of primitive brain. But the researchers have found that after fission, both worms (the one that grew from the tail and the one that grew from the head) "remember" what the parent worm had learned. This implies that the *tail* of the original worm contained part, or at least was able to transmit part, of that worm's knowledge.

How does one go about showing that the tail of a worm contains some aspect of memory? It's not easy. You can't just walk up to a decapitated planarian and say, "How's tricks?"

In one series of experiments, worms are trained to react to sudden bursts of light. While planarians have light-sensitive organs, they have neither lenses nor retina, so that their sensing of light is probably a simple diffused light-dark reaction rather than more sophisticated pattern recognition. Ordinarily, shining a light on one of these worms will cause little or no reaction, but through training they can be taught to react. Their training makes use of the fact that the worms contract convulsively when a small electric shock is applied to their bodies. So here are two stimuli: light and shock. One produces almost no external reaction and the other produces a violent one. These stimuli form a natural pair for experimentation with conditioning.

The worms are ordinarily kept in small finger bowls, but for the training experiments, a worm is placed in a foot-long plastic trough. In the trough the worm gets a flash of light from two 100-watt bulbs and then an electrical shock. At first the worm responds only to the shock, but after about 150 repetitions the work gets the idea that the light always precedes the shock, and it will contract in response to the light alone, even if the shock is omitted. Now you must judge if the worm has "learned" something in this process. Its response to light is certainly different from its untrained brothers. Within certain limits it can remember to contract in response to light alone. This is classical conditioning, of course, and is suspiciously similar to the way parents "teach" proper behavior to a baby.

Professor James McConnell and his associates in the Psychology Department at the University of Michigan trained a group of worms by this shock stimulation method. The worms were then divided into two sub-groups, which I will call A and B. The A's were put back into their finger bowls and allowed to remain idle. Each worm in the B group was cut in half and allowed to regenerate. The worm halves grew back into full worms in about two weeks as expected, and the experimenters allowed another two weeks for further recuperation. Then, four weeks after they were trained, group A and the regenerated group B were again subjected to the light-shock treatment. Group A, having lain idle for four weeks, remembered to contract to light alone after forty more lessons with some worm-to-worm variability. Clearly they remembered something, since 70% fewer lessons were required this time. Then McConnell and his group tried the regenerated worms. The old head/new tail worms remembered as well as the uncut worms. Okay, that seems logical enough; after all they still had the brain that received the training. Then the new head/old tail worms were tested. These worms *also* took only forty lessons to remember their old learned behavior. So, at this point, the experimenters knew that the regenerated worms could be retrained as easily as the control worms, and, more startling, that the old tails somehow retained as much as the old heads. How can memory be carried forward in any place but the brain?

Other groups in other universities demonstrated the same type of retention using different laboratory apparatus. Both tails and heads remembered equally again.

Two other experiments should be described because they seem to shed a little light on this apparent inheritance of learning. First, picture this: a worm is trained, then cut in half. Two worms now grow back from these halves as before. Suppose these two worms are cut in half again. Of the four resulting worms two would be composed of worm halves that were not part of the original worm at all. What do you suppose would happen if these two worms, built completely of regenerated parts, were retrained? Right. Even these worms show significant retention of learning.

Second, picture this: planarians can be cannibals. In a series of experiments, untrained cannibal worms were fed chopped-up trained worms. Remarkably, through some process we do not understand, the worms which ate their trained cousins learned to contract to light in a period significantly shorter than completely "virgin" candidates.

So, in summary, these experiments suggest:

(1) Worms can learn and retain at least a portion of this information over a period of several weeks.

(2) This learning can be passed on in asexual reproduction.

(3) Memory is associated with portions of the body not involving the brain.

(4) Memory can be transmitted in the form of food.

Now take a deep breath and ask just where the seat of memory really is. Is it the brain? If the brain of an untrained worm is removed, it cannot learn rapidly, if at all. Lacking a brain, a worm does not move well. Yet, if the brain is removed from a trained worm, it still remembers to react. Thus, it appears that the brain is probably necessary to efficient learning, but is not necessary for memory. How is the information stored, then? Biochemically within the cells of the body, perhaps? This might account for the passing on of information as part of the regeneration process.

If all of this is true, perhaps the theory of evolution itself could stand some scrutiny. We have *known* since Darwin that knowledge, an acquired characteristic, cannot be passed on as part of our inheritance. The worm experiments may lead one to question this basic and universal truth. Yet the results of the experiments are not completely conclusive: worms born through the sexual union of trained parents have not yet been checked for the presence of part of the memory of their parents' learning. If a test of the progeny of sexual reproduction produced positive results, we would certainly question our old ideas of heredity. Even with this bit of missing data, the question has to be recognized. Reproduction through asexual fission is reproduction nevertheless, and the theory of evolution does not distinguish between the possible modes of parenthood. But geneticists might argue effectively that genetics is the science of sexual reproduction.

I asked Dr. McConnell about the missing "memory-after-sex" experiment. He wrote me:

> Planarians can be bred in captivity, but most people in the past haven't been too successful. However, a zoologist friend of mine in Oklahoma ran across a lovely species that mates all year round even in the lab. We've been using these animals regularly in our work for a couple of years now and have hatched thousands of the beasts. We've hatched other specimens too (as have zoologists for years) but the others are seasonal, while the Oklahoma worms are continuous in their sexual behavior. We haven't tried the "memory-after-sex" study yet for a number of reasons . . . chiefly because there have been other things seemingly more pressing and because nobody would believe us if the damned thing did come out anyhow. We would have done it in the past, but all the worms we tried (prior to getting the Oklahoma beasts) stopped mating as soon as we started handling them. The Sooner-Worms apparently will mate even after being trained. We'll get to that study someday.

Dr. Carl Jung, the psychologist, has a basic feature of his view of psychology, the collective unconscious—that subconscious collection of stories and thoughts and predispositions that the race of man holds in common by virtue of being man. This material is, he believes, inherited, and accounts for recurrent motifs in mythology, and in the symbology of tribes and races widely diverse in their chronology and geography. If Dr. McConnell is right, perhaps this collective unconscious is not a static inheritance, but a dynamic racial storehouse which is added to or modified slightly in each succeeding generation so that the tides of man are carried by all men, and the race today, for better or worse, remembers.

With ideas like this being possible, barely possible, as a result of his work, it is no wonder that McConnell has run into some vicious opposition. The pattern of this opposition will soon be familiar to the reader. Some snickers of disbelief and "why don't you use your time for something worth-while." Refusal of space for publication of the results of his experimentation. Outright antagonism. Vested interests. Staked reputations. And all for the sake of a worm.

McConnell freely admits that he didn't know the fields of invertebrate physiology, or the biochemistry of regeneration, in depth at the outset of his work. Knowledge in these fields would have made life easier, not because his experimental work would have changed, but because he could have used the proper jargon, the "in" phrases, when first reporting his work. But then, if he had been expert in these fields, he might not have gone into this pioneering work because, clearly, "worms can't retain learning." He had the advantage of selective ignorance. As one zoologist said of his early work, "It can't be true: if it were, a zoologist would have done it years ago."

One of the world's greatest authorities on invertebrate physiology, or "dead planarians," is an invertebrate biologist. Because of her reputation in this field, Dr. McConnell sent her some of his early papers, hoping for some sort of endorsement or recommendation, or even debate or just comment on his approach. But he received no answer. On a trip east he decided to stop in for a face-to-face discussion with her. He told me that the discussion went something like this:

"Oh yes, McConnell," she said, "you're the one that did that thing on regeneration."

"Yes, that's right."

"Do you really think they can learn?"

"Yes, I do. Don't you?"

"Well, maybe they can retain what they've learned for five minutes or so," she said.

"Why do you say that?"

"I just do."

"Did you ever train a worm?"

"No."

After this, McConnell sent her more of his published work. Finally she wrote to him and asked him to stop sending these things to her, and please, she said, stop misleading those high school kids. Incidentally, since their meeting she has been sending Dr. McConnell copies of her own stuff.

This interplay never broke into the technical press, so while it may have been frustrating to McConnell, it did not influence a large segment of the scientific community. When a scientist of known reputation decides to carry the battle forward in technical periodicals on the basis of scanty data or personal preconceptions, it is the reputation with greater renown that usually carries the day. What does *winning* mean here? Scientists are busy people. They sometimes form their opinions as we do, on the basis of the statements of people they respect. Thus, when a man of recognized ability contests the results of an unknown, many scientists "turn off" new avenues of research and thought which might have otherwise been opened to them. The unknown, what of him? First, his continued research immediately becomes more difficult. His own university or research institute may begin to raise figurative eyebrows. "Is this guy a kook? Look what Dr. So-and-so says." Funding and resources may suddenly become tighter. In other places experiments that could have added to the original work die a-borning. In the extreme the very means of expression open to the innovator may dry up. Papers are refused, symposia are filled. The promise of being recognized for an original contribution seems suddenly to have moved very far away.

Dr. McConnell told me this story: In 1962, Dr. Melvin Calvin, winner of the Nobel Prize for chemistry, called McConnell to the University of California campus in Berkeley to talk about the Michigan research. McConnell lectured there and Calvin was quite excited about the work because he felt that it might offer some insight into the mystery of the biochemical nature of learning. Such support, if it materialized, would have been very important to McConnell because it would have provided the worm work an aura of respectability, and extended the area of experimental productivity.

Dr. Calvin undertook his own worm research at Berkeley. Dr. McConnell furnished two graduate students to help set up the laboratory and demonstrate techniques established over long years at Michigan. Something happened to turn the work sour. There were personality clashes. The data seemed to be less impressive than that achieved at Michigan. McConnell thinks the Berkeley group became discouraged by the slow progress. Finally, when the students left, the technicians they had been training took over under the leadership of Dr. Edward Bennett. McConnell said, "With no psychologist around, with no one who had a feeling for the worms, the results became even worse. The research wasn't planned well, their attitude in the laboratory was negative to start with, and their interpretation of the data which they did obtain was wrong."

These Berkeley studies were published eventually, and carried the message: Aha, worms can't learn after all. The article appeared in the *Neurosciences Research Program Bulletin* for July-August, 1964, and McConnell calls it vicious and personal. McConnell asks, "How do you fight someone with a Nobel Prize? When there are biases anyhow, doesn't authority always win?"

In their article "Failure to Train Planarians Reliably" Drs. Bennett and Calvin published data from their own worm experiments. They imply that planarians can't learn. They say that "experimental planarians could not be distinguished from naïve." Furthermore, they imply that only a few reports of positive results have appeared before, and most of these, they say, were authored by McConnell or his co-workers and published in a journal dominated by McConnell. A damaging accusation. If they were right and one took the most lenient view, McConnell would be a misguided scientist who somehow misinterpreted his data or misunderstood the behavior of his worms. He would be a man misled by his desire to prove something that wasn't provable. The most extreme view would have McConnell a villainous intellectual fraud, deliberately twisting or inventing data to serve his ends.

What does McConnell have to say? First of all, he was angry with the article, Bennett and Calvin, and the *Bulletin*. The *Bulletin* wouldn't take his reply, as written, he told me. His rebutting manuscript might be accepted, they said, with some rewriting. He felt that with an attack such as this, he should be permitted free expression in the same journal. As a result, he printed and distributed copies of his manuscript himself. This document clearly, very clearly, establishes his position. He says on the subject of the paucity of published reports:

> . . . In truth, then, of the more than fifty studies on planarian learning published during this century, only eighteen or so are found in the *Digest* [a publication of which McConnell is Editor], and only six are primarily negative reports . . . of the fifty studies mentioned above, only ten are by "McConnell and co-workers." . . . In summary, then, it seems odd that Bennett and Calvin would have chosen to cast such serious doubt on the trainability of planarians since, as the above analysis [of published material] indicates, our early studies showing that planarians can learn, that this behavioral change survives cutting and regeneration, and that some part of the training process transfers via cannibalism, are among the most widely replicated and generally confirmed pieces of research in the recent psychological literature . . . More than fifty different experiments have so far been reported in the scientific literature demonstrating that planarians are capable of learning; surely it would be presumptuous of Bennett and Calvin to offer their own set of studies as "proof" that planarians cannot be trained reliably.

It would have been interesting to hear the reply of Bennett and Calvin to this part of McConnell's rebuttal. Since he didn't publish it, no reply is on record. McConnell's point is this: Bennett and Calvin were wrong when they said that the literature didn't support the fact that worms can learn.

Now why didn't the Berkeley worms learn? McConnell's answer: They *did*, but Bennett and Calvin didn't interpret their own data properly! He took their own published data and analyzed it. In the two experiments conducted for Calvin by the Michigan graduate students, the results showed learning of about the same level that McConnell experienced. But, he says:

> . . . Incredibly, not once in their 23 page, data-packed summary of their results do Bennett and Calvin report any statistical analysis of their findings! . . . Even a crude (mathematical) test shows that the improvement is significant at beyond the .001 level of confidence . . . The mean scores . . . clearly describe what most psychologists would call a "typical" learning curve.

Why did they then ignore these two runs? Bennett and Calvin imply that the experimenters subconsciously looked for "proper" performance, since they knew what the worms were supposed to do. Furthermore, there was, as McConnell himself admits, a great variability of performance of the experimental animals.

In a final conclusion on these runs McConnell, with obvious restraint, says:

> . . . Frankly, I do not believe that Bennett and Calvin understand just how complex a phenomenon learning actually is . . . they should not be excused for the numerous mistakes, contradictions, distortions of fact and erroneous conclusions that appear in their paper.

McConnell wrote to Bennett directly to point out these objections. His answer, McConnell says, suggests

> . . . that these authors probably meant to state that they could not always and uniformly reproduce the very high levels of performance sometimes achieved in other laboratories, rather than implying as they did in the original version of their paper that their worms just "couldn't learn."

In a letter to me, Dr. Calvin said that while his article reported an experimental failure, he still is intensely interested

in the relationship between molecular process and structure, and learning and memory. His search for experimental
systems he considers acceptable is continuing.

In another instance, after lecturing at the University of
Indiana, Dr. McConnell's work was challenged by a noted
comparative psychologist on the faculty, who defined learning as discriminative, associative behavior rather than the
behavior which is elicited by classical conditioning. The
debate was hot, but inconclusive. Later, in private, a girl
who had been in the audience came up to McConnell and
told him, in tears, of some experiments she had conducted
under the psychologist while an undergraduate at Indiana.
The worms learned, she said. Why didn't she speak up in
the debate? McConnell asked. She couldn't challenge her
teacher's authority.

And the debates continue. The worms slither on, oblivious
to the semantic nuances and staked reputations that are
racking their would-be trainers.

Dr. James McConnell is a humorous, soft-spoken gentle-
man from Shreveport, Louisiana. He has a small, intellectu-
ally cluttered office at the Mental Health Research Institute
on the campus of the University of Michigan at Ann Arbor.
On his desk are letters and litter, psychological magazines;
a new copy of *The Bio-Chemical Approach to Life* is in his
"in-box," waiting, you suspect, to be read at the rare, first
free moment. At thirty-nine he looks vaguely like a serious
and quiet Dick Van Dyke with horn-rimmed glasses. But
he is a crusading psychologist specializing in worm learning.
As he talks, reviewing the problems he has met in trying to
understand how worms learn and pass on their information,
he leans back in his office chair, relaxed, in an open sport
shirt. He gives you a quiet glimpse into his world of research,
bureaucratic frustrations, and perhaps, the future. In a sense,

he is confronted with the same problem his experiments have evoked: How can the information be passed on?

Professor McConnell has started his own journal of invertebrate psychology. He calls it *The Worm Runner's Digest*. In the vernacular of the psychologist, a "runner" is an experimenter who "runs" animals through a maze; hence, a psychologist who experiments with rats is a rat runner. McConnell and his co-workers are worm runners. *The Worm Runner's Digest* is their contribution to the literature. It is a technical journal like none other you've seen, primarily because Dr. McConnell has a sense of humor. First let me say that the scientific articles about learning, training, and behavior of planarians are of the highest caliber, seriously assembled and presented, and meant to be read by other experimenters in the field. There are serious articles on other subjects too, some of them offbeat, such as a report on the attempt made by Eric Holmes and Gail Gruenberg to condition the plant Mimosa Pudica.

This shrub reacts to a brisk touch by folding its leaves to appear in a wilted condition. These experimenters tried to determine if this reaction could be conditioned, much like Pavlov and his dog which salivated at the sound of a ringing bell. Holmes and Gruenberg used a light touch and an electric shock. If they had been able to train the plants, one might conjure up visions of invading, offensive vegetables as in the best science fiction format, but they say, ". . . four days of training produced no evidence of learning in our brightest plants."

Next to these scientific articles might appear a cartoon showing, for example, two worms, one obviously male and the other female. The male, rejected in love, has a broken heart. The female worm says: "I'm sorry, but it would never work out, Irving. I'm *trained* and you're not."

And then there's the one showing the front end of a dissected worm. He is a bellicose picket, holding a sign. The sign reads: THE END IS COMING.

The *Digest* used to intersperse comic articles among the serious. These were often contributed by other scientists letting off a little steam. They were satires, for the most part, dealing with the rigors of life in the laboratory, the bureaucracy of universities, or just out-and-out scientific spoofs. A few titles will illustrate the point:

> The Effect of Background Noise on the Detection of Cork-popping by Larry Newberry
>
> Platy and Ptiny Planarian, A Story for Children by Marie Jenkins
>
> The Truth about Mendel, or Hollyhocks and the Forebears by Peter Driver

Some readers, perhaps because of their highly tuned sophistication, found it difficult to distinguish between the real and the spoof articles. To avoid this confusion, McConnell now prints half of *The Worm Runner's Digest* right side up, for the straight technical articles, and half of it upside down, for the comic articles. There are still some unhappy readers who feel that humor has absolutely no place in a technical journal, or more seriously, that the presence of humor makes the *Digest* nontechnical. In fact, to some it implies that all of McConnell's work is a joke, not to be taken seriously. About this aspect, McConnell has written:

> . . . We've gotten in a fair amount of hot water from time to time because we gored somebody's sacred cow, or because some of our peers who fail to see anything funny about *anything* scientific refused to take us seriously. These are the sorts of people who, finding the *Digest* half-filled

with humor, refuse to credit the lab reports or the theoretical articles with being "worthwhile." Who'd publish in something like the *Digest*, after all, when it's just a "joke" magazine?

*The Worm Runner's Digest* was born in 1959, when *Newsweek* ran a brief report on some of the work being done at the University of Michigan. This article drew more than a hundred letters, most being requests for detailed information on how to train worms. McConnell says that many of these requests came from high school students who wanted to work with planarians in science fair projects. The Michigan group dittoed a summary of their experience up to that date, fourteen pages in all, picked a Latin motto: *Ignotum per Ignotius*, labeled the purple pages Vol. 1, No. 1, and unknown to the originators, the journal had started. Even though this first issue was to have been the start and the finish, contributions for the next issue started coming in from readers, and as Dr. McConnell puts it, "one damned thing led to another."

Then Dr. McConnell's work and the *Digest* itself got some publicity in *Time* and *The Saturday Evening Post*. After the subscription list passed a thousand, the group started charging for the magazine. Today there are almost 1200 subscribers who pay $1.50 per issue or $5.00 for four issues. Dr. McConnell says:

> . . . There are many serious and sober scientific journals which have a larger circulation; I would guess that few of these, however, are as widely *read* as is the *Digest*. If you've ever scanned the typical scientific publication, you'll really understand why.

The *Digest* has recently become refereed, meaning that each piece is reviewed by a jury before it is accepted for publication. This was necessary, McConnell feels, because of the persistent criticism that pro-planarians, and only those of a special ilk at that, were the sole judges of the adequacy of the material to be printed. This narrowed the magazine's perspective, and raised unnecessary questions about bias and accuracy. Hence, the referees. These are eminent men and women in the field, obviously not hostile to the subject of planarian learning. Some of the fun has gone out of the magazine since the early days because of this rigor, but the *Digest* still exists as an open document, an extroverted, minority report, perhaps, in the field of invertebrate learning.

It would be easy to make spectacular extrapolations about Professor McConnell's work. If memory, or at least the ability to acquire information, is not solely an attribute of the physiological structure of the brain, then perhaps a means can be found to speed up the process of human learning. Can we project a time when, through chemical or molecular means, the brain of a child will open to new learning and absorb instruction and acquire all the information of generations past in a few weeks?

Today we have an information explosion. Before any serious researcher tackles a new project he must know all of the important work which has preceded his own. Furthermore, while his work is in progress, he must keep up with advances and new data being generated not only in his own, but in overlapping disciplines as well. The time may come when so much information must be absorbed before any new creative effort is initiated that the period available for contribution will be severely limited, perhaps even extinguished. Of course, large automated data storage centers will greatly increase man's ability to file and recall information, but even with these machine memories available, a man, somewhere, must know what to ask for. Dead storage won't facilitate research.

There are two ways to avoid the stagnation which will accompany "information saturation." These are: First, increased specialization, the narrowing of fields of interest to permit acquiring knowledge in depth rather than breadth. This, of course, is already happening. With it come the attendant problems of limiting interdisciplinary communications. This creates artificial forests of vision-limiting trees, and causes a lack of appreciation of the effects of certain enterprises on other parallel fields of human endeavor. An example is the case of pollution of a lake and the killing of its fish through the use of a mosquito pesticide—the entomologist didn't talk to the ichthyologist, or perhaps didn't even know his language. The alternate approach is to extend the scope of information available to an individual. Just having it available in a computer won't solve the problem; he must *know* it. If chemicals can increase this *knowing*, this requisite recall, we can look to a new plateau of achievement.

The phenomenon of "plateaus" is interesting. In learning Morse code, for example, a student will reach a low speed of code sending and reception when he has simply memorized the code characters. When he hears a group of dots and dashes, he searches his memory for a "fit" and writes down the proper letter translation. This is the first plateau and his speed stays roughly constant until, through practice, the search becomes "automatic" and he hears and sends groups of dots-dashes, the groups being individual letters rather than disembodied sounds. This is his second plateau. As his proficiency increases, he begins to send and hear groups of letters or even whole words.

The analogy to the information explosion is clear. We are

approaching the first plateau. A man can teach his child
what men have known before in perhaps twenty to twenty-
five years if the field of specialization is kept narrow enough.
If we want to generalize rather than specialize, and want,
for example, to produce an individual who is an in-depth
expert in atomic physics, social science and politics, clearly
we have reached saturation today. The answer: Speed up
learning and increase memory span. How? Perhaps, as Dr.
McConnell's experiments suggest, it can be done chemically:
a pill, taken before class or reading a book, that puts our
receptors, our internal data storage, whatever this may be,
in the *comprehend and store* position.

There is a model today of a chemical stimulant to memory
in the psychiatrist's use of the drug sodium pentothal. Although Dr. McConnell's work is proceeding down different
lines, this usage illustrates at least a direct interrelationship
between memory and body chemistry. Under the hand of a
practical psychiatrist, a patient who has had sodium pentothal injected into his blood enters a semiconscious, half
awake trance and can be led back over his past, recalling
consciously forgotten memories.

In the same context, the drug LSD, given in very minute
amounts, can significantly alter the subject's awareness or
consciousness of the present. A dosage of only 100 micro-
grams can evoke a hallucinatory experience. This again
illustrates the dependency of mental functions on a very delicate balance of chemicals in the body.

There is a hint, a mere suggestion, in this work of the
planarian researchers, that memory can be transferred directly, that the pill will contain not only the mind-opening
instructions, but the data, the information itself. The theories
of memory and learning today are manifold. No one knows
the manner by which a melody or an equation or the scent

of a flower is stored and remembered. Some scientists believe memory is a function of the way certain molecules are arranged within cells. DNA (deoxyribonucleic acid) molecules are long, spiral chains resembling two twisted, intermeshed spiral staircases. The arrangement of the compounds along the strands determines what the function of the cell will be, i.e., what it will manufacture, and the heredity of the cell's descendants. This concept of the DNA molecule is known as the Watson-Crick model for which they shared the Nobel Prize in 1962.

Now clearly these DNA molecules supply the cell with a kind of memory, a genetic memory. The seat of memory of sensory experience is more elusive, however.

The DNA molecules are located in the nuclei of living cells. Another long molecular chain, RNA (ribonucleic acid), derives its shape and chemical make-up by fitting into the molecular pattern offered by the DNA chain. The RNA then moves from the nucleus into the cytoplasm, the outer part of the cell, where by virtue of its shape and electrical charge, proteins are assembled from the contiguous chemical raw materials. In addition to this function, there is some reason to believe that the RNA molecules may contain the coded information which represents sensory memory.

In one set of worm experiments, five hundred animals were trained by the light-shock method. These animals were then reduced chemically and the RNA extracted from their bodies. It was injected into untrained worms. These injected worms were then given the light-shock training at the same time as a group of "virgin" control worms. The injected worms showed themselves to be significantly smarter than their unprepared brothers. In other experiments, the use of chemicals which retard RNA synthesis in cells was shown to impair memory. Other researchers at UCLA have extended these RNA experiments to rats with the same type of results.

But this work does not prove that RNA is the seat of memory; it shows only that manipulation of this molecule can affect memory. Some other undiscovered mechanism may yet be involved. But suppose this is the mechanism. Suppose that the RNA molecule is modified somehow by sensory experience. It would then manufacture proteins and stimulate neurons a little differently than before. Enough of these bits of information, called up and joined together by the central nervous system switchboard, may be, to the brain, say a melody, or an equation, or the scent of a rose. Furthermore, as Dr. McConnell's experiments suggest, the altered molecules may circulate throughout the body and thus the severed tail of a worm can grow a head that somehow remembers.

But memory must also surely reside in the brain as well. Dr. Wilder Penfield, who performed pioneering research in the identification of the function of various portions of the brain, found that electrical stimulation of certain regions of the cortex would force a patient's consciousness to elicit precise memory of past events. The recollection under stimulation wasn't a vague let-me-see kind of experience; it was almost a reliving of the event, complete with sound and feeling. It was as though a tape recorder were being turned on. The stimulated memory was called out from storage on command, and played back in real time. It could be an important or trivial event. As long as the current was kept on, the former day replayed itself, with beauty, orchestras, barking dogs, love and hate, more vivid than ordinary dulled unaided memory. Where does memory lie?

With our present state of knowledge, the mechanism of memory is unknown, but McConnell's and Wilder's experiments suggest that perhaps, one day, there may be a treatment, rather a course, in physics or geopolitics or tolerance, in which the markers are all put in the right places. Then the education of a man could go on from the base of all which humanity had learned to that point in time.

The danger of such a tool is immediately obvious. Who is to be the programer? What attitudes do we want this century? There was a time when we *knew* the world was flat and that pain in a surgical operation was right and proper because it was God's will—would we have programed these? Can we program skepticism? Can we avoid programing political subservience?

Finally, Dr. McConnell's work raises the possibility that memory, knowledge and attitudes, in fact, all that's known or learned in one generation, can be transferred directly to the next through heredity. If we could find out what special mechanism is involved in transferring information during reproduction, perhaps we could reinforce the effect, and cause learning of a discrete and substantive nature to be carried over from father to son. If we can develop this trick of inheritance, perhaps society could distill its moral judgment and the lessons in value learned by one generation would be the baseline values of the next. What is wisdom but lessons in value; can a son be born as wise as his father? The son could really follow in his father's footsteps, building on what he and the race before had learned. The world then would be an expanding bank of knowledge and experience that would eventually be limited only by the capacity of the brain itself.

# (4

# SHORT CUT
# TO
# NIRVANA

When the race of man existed as groups of nomadic tribes, wandering over deserts and through jungles, every growing thing must have been an experimental food. Certainly some of the experiments must have ended in failure; some foods were poisonous. Others proved nourishing and eventually man learned how to cultivate them. But there was another strange class of plant that he found; these produced reactions in him that seemed to bring the very soul out of his body, extend his consciousness and perception, bring up hallucinations of vivid colors, of wild sounds, imaginary animals and wars and gods. No wonder these strange foods were given a very special place in these civilizations.

Magical mushrooms have been traced back thousands of

years. Archaeologists have found stone artifacts in the shape of mushrooms in the Guatemalan Mayan culture, and while some believe that these are phallic symbols, a common view today is that these objects represent the remnant of a mushroom worship cult dating back to 1000 B.C. It is not improbable that the first crop man ever raised as a commercial venture was hallucinogenic mushrooms. In ancient Greece the wild orgies of Diogenes may have been stimulated by mushrooms. These magic mushrooms are still grown in Mexico. They are called Teonanacatl, God's flesh. They come in several varieties that can be selected and graded for specific hallucinatory responses. They are from the family of dung fungus, Psilocybe mexicana, and produce muscular relaxation, along with illusions of color, hilarity, alteration of time and space, and isolation.

But the pantry of these strange foods only begins with mushrooms. In the West Amazon, a vine, Tetrapterys methstica, is harvested and beaten into a pulp which forms the basis for a drink the natives call *Yaje*. Supposedly, it is the strongest of the hallucinogens. It is taken for a dash of bravery. It has alleged telepathic properties.

The Incas of Peru grew *Datura*, an herb, and added the seeds to their fermented drink *Chicha*. It produced violent reactions which were associated with spirit visitations. Spirits were not to be fooled with, so this drink was used to make children behave properly: "Do as I say, or you'll have to take some *Datura*, and your dead Uncle Henry will take care of you . . ."

Three teenagers in California were rushed to the hospital recently after they were found screaming and laughing on a street corner. They believed that multicolored bugs were crawling all over them. They had been chewing the seeds of the *Datura* weed. City fathers went out to survey the local weed crop, but it was so plentiful that it could not be eradicated.

Mexicans in Oaxaca still use Salvia, a wild plant of the mint family which grows freely on the hills. Our Mexican housekeeper says that when the natives chew it, they go *loco*. It's *muy malo*, but a little bit of it, under the pillow at night, guarantees a good night's sleep.

Mescal Beans or *frijolitos* come from the American southwest and Mexico. They are the dark red seeds of the plant Sophora secundiflora. Botanical historians believe these seeds formed the basis for magical and religious rites among the Indians before *Peyote* came into use. *Peyote* comes from a small cactus which is sliced and dried to form little disks called mescal buttons. It produces kaleidoscopic and colored visions, and forms the basis of a contemporary, functioning religious order, the Native American Church. This sect numbers 200,000 and is composed mostly of American Indians. The mescal buttons are eaten in their church by the congregation as a sort of sacrament; by eating *Peyote* a person can absorb part of the power of god, since God put the power in the cactus in the first place. This, of course, has an obvious analogy to the Catholic sacraments in which the churchgoers absorb part of the power of God by eating a specially blessed wafer which represents His flesh.

This religion is in force today. It exists here, now, in the United States.

Peyotism embraces the principles of Christianity and may be as old as Judaism. The basic beliefs of Peyotism include some familiar tenets: there is one God, the Great Spirit who created the universe and man and controls all facets of destiny. God put some of his manna into *Peyote* and gave it to the Indians as his special gift. By eating *Peyote*, under the proper ritual conditions, a person can absorb some of God's spirit. This spirit manifests itself as a supernatural revelation, a mystical rapture, during which God himself or one of his spirits can reveal some religious or ethical dogma.

Dr. J. S. Slotkin, associate professor of Social Sciences at the University of Chicago, has made several deep studies into the anthropology of peyotism among the Menomini Indians of the U.S. Midwest. He described his own participation in their ceremonies in a monograph to the American Philosophical Society:

> The peyote bag was passed around with instructions to "take two"; later it was passed again with the instructions— "Take as many as you like." I began to work on mine and it was bitter from the first bite. I simply couldn't swallow the hard bits of peyote so I softened it as much as I could and managed to slip some of it down . . . In this way I had eaten four buttons . . . They tasted like dried pieces of orange peel. As the second round began, I leaned over to the man next to me and asked him how long it was before it began to take effect. He said, "About half an hour," so I passed by the second round in order to see what the effect would be of those I had already taken, before trying any more. The third round I took another four, but before I finished them all, one tasted so bitter that I felt that if I were to swallow it it would turn my stomach. I don't know if I happened to pick a particularly bitter one, or whether I had been satiated and any more was distasteful . . .
>
> The rite lasts all night, and is highly formalized. One man acts as high priest or "leader," and he has the help of three or four assistants . . .
>
> It is remarkable how all the other components cooperate in heightening the effect of the Peyote. The shape of the tipi, the perspective presented by the tipi ridgepoles, the acoustics of the tipi, the flickering fire which burns low and then becomes bright as more wood is added by the fire chief, the sparks flying upward and dying out as they reach the top of the tipi, the shadows cast by the people against the

tipi wall, the odor of cedar from the cedar boughs and incense, the character of the songs, the softness and quality
of the singing, the rhythm and timbre of the gourd and
water drum, the position in which the people sit—all har-
monize with the effects produced by the Peyote.

After midnight I began to notice the effects of the Peyote
. . . There were slight visual effects; the fire was the most
beautifully colored I've ever seen, and the shadows cast by
the fire flickered in time to the drumming . . . Suddenly
. . . the drumming seemed to be coming from inside of me.
I paid some attention to this, and discovered that the distinction between myself and non-self disappeared when I closed
my eyes . . .

When I concentrated on anything, all my immediate experience fused with it harmoniously, with no distinction between internal and external aspects of the experience. I
found it very easy to become absorbed in any idea which
I contemplated . . .

My mouth, then my gastric tract, and finally my whole
body, felt very fresh—like the effect of peppermint flavored
toothpaste, but extended to the rest of my body as well. I
didn't feel elated or depressed . . . I was able to sit in one
position for hours on end, without food . . .

Dr. Slotkin interviewed the followers of the Native American Church by living among them and participating in their
rites. He is one of the few white men ever permitted to
gather these data at so intimate a level. From his observations he believes that *Peyote* is neither an intoxicant nor a
narcotic. Furthermore, its continued use does not seem to
build up tolerance; that is, it appears that the dosage can
remain constant for the same psychological effect.

The tremendous increase in perception which comes with
the taking of hallucinogenic drugs has led a number of artists
to experiment with these sensations in an effort to understand themselves and their art, to plumb the limits of their

own capabilities to visualize, to feel, and to describe. Author and philosopher Aldous Huxley took Mescaline, a derivative of *Peyote,* as an experiment in experience.

He took four-tenths of a gram of Mescaline in half a glass of water. Half an hour later he began to see golden lights, slowly dancing. Then, for the better part of a day, the drug held sway. He has written vividly about his sensations. For example, when he looked around the room, he saw his books, ordinary books which had rested on the shelves. Yet these were now:

> . . . Red books, like rubies; emerald books; books bound in white jade; books of agate; of aquamarine, of yellow topaz; lapis lazuli books whose color was so intense, so intrinsically meaningful, that they seemed to be on the point of leaving the shelves to thrust themselves more insistently on my attention . . .

There was no concept of time, no space.

> That chair—shall I ever forget it? Where the shadows fell on the canvas upholstery, stripes of a deep but glowing indigo alternated with stripes of an incandescence so intensely bright that it was hard to believe that they could be made of anything but blue fire. For what seemed an immensely long time I gazed without knowing, even without wishing to know, what it was that confronted me. At any other time I would have seen a chair barred with alternate light and shade. Today the percept had swallowed up the concept. I was so completely absorbed in looking, so thunderstruck by what I actually saw, that I could not be aware of anything else . . . The event was this succession of azure furnace doors separated by gulfs of unfathomable gentian. It was inexpressibly wonderful, wonderful to the point, almost, of being terrifying. And suddenly I had an inkling of what it must feel like to be mad.

And on the emotional aspects:

I was seeing what Adam had seen on the morning of his creation—the miracle, moment by moment, of naked existence . . .

To (some takers of this drug) is revealed the glory, the infinite value and meaningfulness of naked existence, of the given, unconceptualized event. This is as near, I take it, as a finite mind can ever come to "perceiving everything that is happening everywhere in the universe."

These episodes illustrate the basic mystical attribute of the hallucinogens: the ability to detach the "real" self, the soul, the ego, from the corporeal body. Almost all primitive religions, and many contemporary religions, use drugs to promote this detachment. This ability to stand aloof from the role-playing of life and become one with the world, more than oneness, completely fused, marks a religious experience of the deepest intensity. It is the Dharma-Body of the Buddhist, the Beatific Vision, the Mind at Large, the revelation, the Tibetan Clear Light; in other words, it is the transcendence of self.

And that is what this chapter is about: the potential emergence of a new religion for the West based on the use of drugs.

Mescaline is the active element in *Peyote*. Its physiological action in the body is almost as mysterious as the psychological reaction it provokes. Apparently it affects the enzyme balance in the brain and reduces the amount of glucose available. Glucose, of course, is a sugar which the brain utilizes constantly. When this food is withheld from the brain, somehow perception is amplified and whatever it is we call "self" moves from within us to the outside. There are certain similarities between the emotions experienced by the takers of hallucinogenic drugs and the classic schizophrenic. Schizophrenia is characterized by withdrawal, apathy, and daydreaming or hallucinating. To external appearances, the taker of hallucinogenic drugs withdraws, becomes contemplative, and of course, hallucinates.

It would be an oversimplification to say that this apparent similarity of symptoms means that Mescaline can induce clinical schizophrenia. Nevertheless, the similarities are real and apparent, and neuropsychiatric researchers are probing this relationship.

In discussing the relationship of body chemistry to mental health, it is worth mentioning one experiment of a most striking nature which illustrates that there is a door, a very important door, yet to be unlocked. In 1956 a unique protein substance was isolated from the blood of schizophrenics. This protein was then injected into the blood stream of two male volunteers to determine if some psychotic effects could be transmitted in this way. One of the volunteers immediately lapsed into paranoid delusions of persecution; the other, within a few seconds after the injection, fell into a catatonic state, and hallucinated in the manner of a schizophrenic. Both recovered in about two hours.

What does it mean? Perhaps, someday, psychosis can be catalogued and treated chemically or through the alteration of diet. These very big stakes have led the researchers to probe deeply into the nature of hallucinogenic drugs.

There are three major hallucinogenic drugs in use today. These are: Mescaline, which we have already examined; Psilocybin, which was first isolated from Mexican mushrooms and then synthesized in 1958 by the Swiss chemist, Albert Hofmann; and D-lysergic acid diethylamide, or LSD, the most potent of the hallucinogens which was also synthesized by Dr. Hofmann. He isolated this drug during his experiments with ergot, a fungus that attacks rye and other grasses. During this work Dr. Hofmann absorbed some of this chemical, probably through his skin. The effect was so strange he purposely swallowed some and experienced for the first time an LSD voyage into perception, introspection, and "grace" which Huxley describes so well. Dr. Hofmann thought he was going crazy.

LSD is much more powerful than Mescaline or Psilocybin. Doses as small as four millionths of an ounce can cause "The Experience." Sensory impressions are intense, almost painful. The amplifier which is the brain has its volume control turned up. Not that sounds are louder, or sights brighter; they are simply more intrinsically meaningful. The folds in a piece of cloth suddenly have infinite meaning; texture is significant, something to be savored, retained, studied; one subject waded out into the ocean to feel the waves wash around her ankles, to hear and know the power of the ocean; another sat for endless hours studying the leaf from a tree, sensing the leafness in this specimen, becoming one with the leaf and all leaves. There is also a release from ego, a figurative psychological death. In this phase the super-conscious can tackle and understand the meaning of life, converse with God, and reach a state of oneness with all men, and things of all time and for all time.

Yet there are people who do not sense this elevated state, but rather see demons and feel stark terror. They sink into a ghoulish, frightening, hideous torment.

> . . . I can't convey the horror of it except by analogy, says one such subject. Imagine you were forced to look on helplessly while monsters hacked your children to bits. Intensify the emotion by a thousandfold and you'll have some inkling of my ordeal . . .

The direction in which the trance proceeds, whether it goes to the regions beyond heaven or to the levels below the basest hell depends primarily on the predisposition of the subject, what he expects, and the way he is led by his "gate-keep," his "ground control," the experiment supervisor. Recent sufferers of yellow jaundice are supposedly particularly susceptible to the negative-going experience. If a taker expects "kicks," he will usually find them and this has led to illicit use of the hallucinogenic drugs.

Apparently, illicit LSD can be obtained from Canadian sources. There is also some speculation that LSD is being home-brewed. While this process is difficult, some users insist that it is being made at home and in university labs in vast amounts. Another source is morning glory seeds, which contain a natural hallucinogen, monoethylamide.

There is a parallel between social usage of narcotics such as heroin and unsupervised use of LSD. The LSD user seems, in general, to have a better education than his addicted counterpart. He, of course, is not physically dependent on the drug; yet within his subgroup, almost identical patterns of habitual use, mores, "hip" language, proselytizing can be found. A recent sociological study of the behavior of LSD users disclosed that some "black market" users had aesthetic and religious experiences; others, on occasion, sank to pure hedonism:

> . . . these interpersonal delights became quite specific as the partying people took off their clothes and played romantic roulette. The intimacies might be rather public— on the front lawn, on the living room floor, or with six on a bed. Given these varieties of play and euphoria, it is no wonder that a majority of the informal black-market sample (of users) said that orgiastic excitement was a feature of LSD use.

Now we must leave, for a moment, the world of hallucinogens and look at a piece of modern psychology. Dr.

Timothy Leary was a brilliant young psychologist at Harvard. His early major work, *Interpersonal Diagnosis of Personality,* is widely quoted and read by contemporary psychologists. He took his Ph.D. in clinical psychology at the University of California, and, shortly afterwards, was appointed research director at the Kaiser Foundation Hospital in Oakland, California, specializing in psychotherapy. In 1959 he joined the staff at Harvard, and worked there in the Center for Research in Personality under Dr. David C. McClelland.

Dr. Leary searched for the meaning and understanding of psychological behavior in terms of "games" and "roles." To him human behavior could be viewed as a series of games. In the sense that he uses the word, a game is not an amusement; quite the contrary, the games we play are deadly serious. Our games are the real world. As we go about our business of living we all fall into certain well-bounded patterns. Except for the instinctual portion of this routine we're following rules just as surely as a ballplayer in a ballgame. Look at it this way: I'm writing a book. This is the author-game. My wife plays the wife-game. The scientist, the science-game. The ballplayer the ballgame. In each case the players follow certain rules and expect to achieve certain goals. Each game has its own ritual and jargon. Let's follow this analogy through for, say, a dentist.

The dentist has his stereotype game-rules fairly well defined for him. As long as he follows the stereotype rules he can go on drilling teeth. He must be well dressed, respectable. His armpits must not smell, his nails must not be dirty. He must not wear stained smocks. He must complete so many years of college—these are the rules. The dentist-game has its own jargon (caries, dentifrice, root canal, retainer, orthodontist) and ritual ("acid-makes-cavities . . . a full set of mouth X-rays would be in order, I think . . .").

Obviously the analogy is not perfect. In sport-pleasure games the rules are well stated; in real-life games they are not. In sport-pleasure games, the goals are clear; in real life they are not. This is precisely the problem, says Leary. To be effective, to avoid anxiety and understand our own motivations, we should give our real life games the luxury of definition and bounding, which we realize are necessary when we play. In baseball a player signs a contract for a period of performance. The standards which he must meet are clean; if he hits under .200 he will probably be sent back to the minors. If the rules of baseball are ineffective there are means available for changing them. But in real life we try to fill hazy roles and pursue vague goals unlimited in space and time. And how can we change the rules of our role if we don't even know we're playing?

This game concept can lead to workable theories of psychology, means for developing a system of release when the game becomes too tough. In this framework, a person can change his behavior by understanding the rules, knowing the rituals, the jargon, the other players and the bases they are covering. A person can literally tear up his game contract and sign with a new club. He can improve his batting average if he knows that he's swinging at a ball.

Whether or not this view of personality and behavior can lead to new insight into understanding the complex ways in which people interact, is unimportant at this point. The fact is that Leary articulated this game theory with great force. He saw in it a way to tell people about themselves, a way to improve their relationships with one another. After all, if people could see degenerative human activity as nonessential to the structure of their games, maybe, just maybe, the rules could be changed.

Leary was spending the summer of 1960 in a rented house
in Cuernavaca, Mexico. A friend of his from the University
of Mexico, an anthropologist, visited him carrying a little bag
full of sacred mushrooms. Leary had been prejudiced against
the use of drugs, and the artificial probing of minds by other
psychologists. Nevertheless, his friend was a competent person and Leary felt secure with him, trusted him. He ate nine
of the mushrooms and the next five hours changed his life.

> . . . I realized I had died . . . that I, Timothy Leary, the
> Timothy Leary game, was gone. I could look back and see
> my body on the bed. I relived my life, and re-experienced
> many events I had forgotten. More than that, I went back
> in time in an evolutionary sense to where I was aware of
> being a one-celled organism. All of these things were way
> beyond my mind.

The connection between this experience and his own psychological theories were obvious at once.

This is an Eastern idea, a mystical concept. To understand
it fully requires self-abstraction, a detachment, a standing
off from life to gaze into the senseless torrent of our own
emotions and grasp the image of our aimless running from
nameless fear to nameless goal. How then do we achieve this
detachment and understanding? Leary says:

> . . . There are many methods for expanding consciousness
> beyond the game limits . . . expose yourself to some great
> trauma that shatters the gamesmanship out of you. Birth by
> ordeal is a well documented phenomenon. The concentra-
> tion camp experience has done this for some of our wisest
> men. Physical traumas can do it. Electric shock. Extreme
> fatigue. Live in another and very different culture for a
> year where your roles and rituals and language just don't
> mean a thing . . .
>
> (But) the most efficient way to cut through the game struc-
> ture of Western life is through the use of drugs.

The use of drugs—here—is the idea. Drugs can speed up the process of detachment, dwarf the techniques of psycho-analytic talking, and lead to Eastern mystical understanding of life and self. Drugs can show us the sense and senseless-ness of our roles and the petty games we play. It is in this context that the bright young psychologist, Timothy Leary, started experimenting with hallucinogenic drugs at Harvard.

Leary drafted his first research program in the fall of 1960. Aldous Huxley, who was in residence at M.I.T. at the time, came over to Harvard and participated in the original planning of the project. Huxley advocated conducting the experiments in a humanistic rather than a clinical setting. The work at Harvard consisted of two basic sets of experi-ments using Psilocybin.

In one experiment, over one hundred and fifty subjects took the drug. Here the idea was to observe reactions to an alien experience. Leary was interested in the language his subjects would use to describe their feelings and hallucina-tions; he was interested in the way they would react to understanding the game.

Who were the volunteers? They were distinguished in-tellectuals, scholars, graduate students, artists, and medical doctors. They came seeking pure deep experience, seeking to understand the game; some came motivated by nothing more than simple curiosity.

In order to put the subjects at ease, the experimenters took the drug at the same time as the subjects; this elimi-nated what Leary called "the subject-object issue." (Leary dislikes the word "subjects," he prefers "collaborator.") The participants were told all that was known about the drug to remove mystery from the adventure. The environment sur-rounding the test was made homelike and all possible rigid-ity and formality were removed from the testing situation.

Leary was trying to promote a positive-going experience; if his subjects had had the wrong attitude before the experiment, they might have sunk into the morass of hideous nightmares of the negative experience. The tests were successful.

Leary found that three out of four of his subjects had "happy" and "insightful" reactions. Ninety-five percent reported "the experience had changed their lives for the better." The most common reaction was the "sudden perception of the effect of abstractions, rituals, and learned game routines. Ecstatic pleasure at being temporarily freed from these limitations. A game-free honesty."

The second experiment that Leary and his co-workers ran involved the rehabilitation of thirty-five inmates of a state prison. Psilocybin in combination with Leary's game-life theory was used in an attempt to make the prisoners aware of the bigger structure of reality and their role in it.

Typically, he would conduct a series of orientation sessions with a group of maximum security prisoners. After perhaps three of these discussion sessions, he would take the drug at the same time as three of the subjects. The other subjects would be present at these drug-taking episodes and serve as observers. Then, after several hours, the observers would take the drug too. The pattern was repeated later. More consultations, then more drugs.

Leary tested the prisoners before and after the therapy. He says:

> . . . We've never had a moment of friction or violence. Why? Because we spent many many hours with them ahead of time, explaining to them what was going to happen. We had members of our staff take the drug with them. The first person to take drugs in Concord State Prison was myself and the reason I did that was to show them we weren't doing anything to them. This was an experience that we believed

in and we'd share it with them. Wherever possible we'd make the experience pleasant. The last time we had a session there we had graduate students from Harvard bring Oriental rugs into the state prison. The guards thought we were nuts. We were bringing in candles and tape recordings with music they asked for. This was to set up a pleasant supporting environment for them to lose their minds. And they proceeded to lose their minds in an esctatic and deeply religious type of experience . . .

We're convinced that our prisoners have authentic, creative mystical experiences. We're convinced that our prisoners, illiterate and untutored, see what Blake saw, or see what Wadsworth saw, or experience what St. John of the Cross experienced. The problem is they have no words. They say: "Wow, Doc. It's out of this world," or, "Whew. I just died and came back again." That's the limits of their vocabulary . . .

(They showed) dramatic decrease in hostility, cynicism, depression, schizoid ideation. Definite increases in optimism, planfulness, flexibility, tolerance, sociability . . . the psilocybin experience made these men aware of the stereo-typed games in which they had been involved, the game of "cops and robbers," the game of being a tough guy, the game of outwitting the law, the game of resentful cynicism.

A check of prisoners a year and a half after the experiment showed that only 22% had returned to prison; the normal rate at the State Prison was 70%.

These results notwithstanding, Leary's relationship with Harvard had been uneasy from the start. At one point, a committee was appointed with the university physician and several prominent professors participating. This group was set up as a protection against rumors relating to improper use of the drug, but even when the group had control of the drugs, rumors persisted. Black marketeers had begun to capitalize on the undergraduates' interest in hallucinogenic drugs. Sugar cubes containing LSD sold for a dollar apiece. The faculty became openly critical of the work. Where were the scientific controls? Maybe the work with the convicts would have been equally effective without the drugs—perhaps it was the counseling sessions that had produced results.

The controversial nature of the work led Leary and his co-workers to move off the campus, away from the university setting. An independent research organization was formed called the International Federation for Internal Freedom (IFIF). The board of directors was composed of eight very prominent scientists, philosophers and religious leaders from Harvard, M.I.T., and divinity schools in the Boston area. The organization first located in a suite in a Boston medical building, but as Dr. Leary put it, "we're being thrown out of there because some of the doctors felt we weren't practicing medicine." Finally, Leary and his major collaborator, Dr. Richard Alpert, were dismissed from the university faculty, because, as *Time* magazine reported, "university authorities agree with the medical profession that the drugs they used are too dangerous for campus experiments." An apparent factor in their dismissal was the use of undergraduates in the experiments, against the instructions of the university. By the time they left Harvard, they had given over 3500 doses of various drugs to over 400 subjects.

In 1963 the group established the IFIF Psychedelic Training Center in the village of Zihuatanejo, Mexico. The group leased the largest hotel in the town, the Catalina. The hotel's bungalows were on a tropical hill, overlooking the broad Pacific beach. There were hammocks and parrots and mangoes, a bar, privacy, since the hotel was a short distance out of town; in short, this was a delightful, restful setting for a peaceful vacation. Tourists had not yet found Zihuatanejo. On a typical day IFIF visitors to the Catalina rose about ten in the morning. They swam in the warm ocean and ate in a relaxed setting. Before lunch they would sketch, or practice yoga exercises, or swim in the ocean again. Siesta followed their three o'clock lunch. In the afternoon they might tour the village or walk along the beach. Guests would share a drink or two before the late dinner which was almost always followed by informal, absorbing discussions which centered around the drug experience, its relationship to life and Eastern mysticism, and the game theory of behavior. Once a week *mariaches* would come in from town and there would be a fiesta. Rules were minimum; this was the IFIF game.

Most of the guests were intellectuals, professional men and their wives. At least one family brought their children to Zihuatanejo. One of the visitors was Joseph J. Downing, a psychiatrist who did not become a member of IFIF. Dr. Leary had readily agreed to let him come to Mexico as an observer. His report, from which some of my earlier comments concerning Zihuatanejo and those following are drawn, is fascinating. He said that members of the group appeared to be serene and happy and were well-behaved, sophisticated people interested in psychology and their experiences. They were seeking an understanding of themselves, a deepening of their religious values, removal of negative personality symptoms, and a strengthening of their positive personality characteristics.

The IFIF staff administered LSD to each visitor about twice a week. The guests were permitted freedom of the hotel and beach while under the influence of the drug. A ritual was formed around a tower which was located on the beach. Generally, one person who was under the influence of the drug was in the tower at all times. To be permitted to take the drug in the tower was a privilege and apparently a source of status in the Catalina community. One staff member told of the time she had to go near the tower, without LSD. She tingled just approaching it; near its base she felt "high," as though she had just taken the drug. The guests all knew who was in the tower at any time; the tower and the "high" man had a mystic validity for the group.

Dr. Leary did not object to publicity for the IFIF center; in fact, he welcomed it. Some of the stories that appeared were not complimentary, as one might well imagine. Clearly the Mexican authorities knew of his operation. Dr. Downing, writing of the expulsion of the group from Mexico, had this to say:

> . . . The IFIF group was certainly not on good terms with the academic psychiatric advisors to Mexican health officials. Dr. Leary believed this lack of amity was largely owing to an unfortunate and unavoidable incident in which he seemed discourteous to an important psychiatrist; however, this also fits into the break with Harvard academicians which occurred at about the same time.

Pressure also came from Oaxaca, the Mexican magic mushroom center. People there were apparently concerned that the overflow from Zihuatanejo would come to Oaxaca and, in pursuing the hallucinogenic mushrooms, profane the sacred native rites.

The final catalyst to their expulsion came from an American visitor who was not accepted at the center; the staff had apparently judged him to be too unstable to receive LSD. He wrote to a reporter in Mexico City, and his letter about the center was published. According to Dr. Downing the letter was inaccurate and full of falsehoods.

> . . . With an impending national election and the constant affronts by American tourists to Mexican pride, the government could not afford to ignore the IFIF group even after

investigation showed the newspaper stories to be false. Therefore, acting entirely within its rights and responsibilities, the government decreed expulsion but acted with courtesy and consideration in doing so.

The group was sent from Mexico in the second week of June 1963. The official grounds were that the group had entered as tourists, not researchers or students.

It was at Zihuatanejo that the hallucinogenic nongame began to take on certain aspects of a religion. IFIF had recognized this connection earlier and used it in Mexico to heighten the Experience and give it more insight and meaning.

The book of instruction for new arrivals at Zihuatanejo was called *The Psychedelic Experience*. It was a manual patterned after the Tibetan *Book of the Dead*. The original book was a description of how to die, or rather what experiences to expect in dying. It was sort of a road map to oblivion. The theory was that if a person knew what to expect as his soul departed from his body, the whole experience could be met with courage. Knowing where to go, the soul would not be left wandering aimlessly but emerge straightway into the "after-death plane." To Leary it was a model of the hallucinogenic experience. If the stimulated psyche knew where to go, it could avoid the hellish negative experience, and emerge into the full glory of enlightenment. The drug experience was a psychological death and rebirth.

Step by step the Psychedelic Experience leads the potential drug taker through the mysteries waiting for him, from the First Bardo, the period of the clear light (a term borrowed from the Tibetan book), to the Second Bardo, the period of hallucinations, to the Third Bardo, the period of re-entry. Within each of these periods various states of mind are discussed such as the more typical visions: the judgment visions, the wrathful visions, and sexual visions. For the traveler who still stumbles on this path to eternity and comes across the wrathful demons, Leary has this advice:

> O nobly born, listen well:
> You are now in the magic theater of heroes and demons.
> Mythical superhuman figures.
> Demons, goddesses, celestial warriors, giants,
> Angels, Bodhisattvas, dwarfs, crusaders,
> Elves, devils, saints, and sorcerers,
> Infernal spirits, goblins, knights and emperors.
> The Lotus Lord of Dance.
> The Wise Old Man. The Divine Child.
> The Trickster, The Shapeshifter.
> The tamer of monsters.
> The mother of gods, the witch.
> The moon king. The wanderer.
> The whole divine theater of figures representing the
>     highest reaches of human knowledge.
> Do not be afraid of them.
> They are within you.
> Your own creative intellect is the master magician of
>     them all.
> Recognize the figures as aspects of your self.
> The whole fantastic comedy takes place within you.
> Do not become attached to the figures.
> Remember the teachings.
> You may still attain liberation.

In this poetry we can see the ethereal figures of Jung's collective unconscious, released by the drug, drifting across the panorama of the mind. We can also see a religion, complete with incense, incantation, mystical figures, and revelation.

After the Mexican government closed the training center at Zihuatanejo, Drs. Leary and Alpert moved back to the United States, and in the quiet town of Millbrook, New

York, opened another consciousness-expanding institution, the Castalia Foundation. The weekend workshops at Castalia would last from six-thirty Friday evening to Sunday afternoon and each participant was "invited to contribute a minimum of seventy-five dollars per weekend." Drugs were no longer used, according to the Foundation's brochure, but sessions were held in which the guests and staff enjoyed simulated psychedelic experiences. These sessions were based on traditional Eastern concepts and relied on the insight gained by some of the staff in their earlier explorations with drugs.

In December 1965, Dr. Leary and his eighteen-year-old daughter, Susan, were stopped while crossing the Mexican border at Laredo, Texas. In searching them, U.S. Customs officers found that Susan was carrying three ounces of marijuana, which Leary claimed was his. Both were brought to trial in federal court and Dr. Leary was fined $40,000 and sentenced to thirty years' imprisonment, the maximum allowable term. This sentence will probably be reviewed after psychiatric examinations are completed.

Castalia was raided by police in April 1966, and Dr. Leary, who was free on bail, was arrested again for "possessing" drugs found in the mansion.

The drive to escape from one's self may be a deeply rooted instinct, a need which was discovered the day after ego came. Someone has called the invention of ego the original sin, because from this purely man-made concept have come all subconcepts of selfishness such as nationalism, war, poverty, acquisitiveness, gluttony, owning, and "momism," to name only a few. In the years since we discovered ego, we have found many ways to escape from it. These methods all have one thing in common: they give man a new experience—a clearly superordinary experience. In their most effective form, they make man forget who he is or what he is—for a few blessed moments they pardon his sin, ego. They lift him into a new realm of awareness and, in their noblest form, make him part of an egoless, nameless cosmic entity from which vantage life has meaning and purpose. Clearly this is akin to religious enlightenment. Contemplation for hours with legs crossed and mind drifting in the manner of the East can produce this awareness. Hallucinogenic drugs are an easier route; they can provide a short cut to Nirvana.

What are some other short cuts? Since our history began, opium, alcohol, hashish, fasting, self-mortification, isolation-contemplation: all of these. Some of these devices send a person down to absolute groveling despair; what matters is the moment, the hour, the day when ego is fled, the sin is no longer a sin, and the self is more than self.

There are other devices, too, that Huxley points out. Perhaps these are less effective, but they are also less ominous. Rhythm, the solemn repeated, endless beat that can lift the soul and drive it into wilder and wider excursions until at last, as surely as opium, the only pleasure is in the beat. Dance, the frenzy by the fire, calling the gods to witness the escape of the souls, the repeated monotony and ecstasy in movement which are echoed today in the Asian dervishes, the Shakers, the Holy Rollers, and in small children, turning on their toes almost endlessly out of pure joy, until they fall dizzy beyond standing. Sex, when the ego leaves and the duo is supreme, when for a fleeting moment self is the absolute universe.

Hallucinogenic drugs forgive the sin of ego in a most spectacular way. They are not habit forming. They are as old as history. So why shouldn't we take the short cut? Here is the major argument against drugs: A man escaping via drugs cannot create. When he is "turned on" he appears to withdraw as a schizophrenic; when he feels he has broken free, he is in fact a slave to his delusions. As disturbing as it may be, ego leads to creativity. The anxiety it provokes leads us to accomplishment; thus our sin is also our blessing.

Once a group of scientists implanted two fine wires in the brain of a rat. The electrodes were centered in the rat's pleasure center. When a small electrical charge was applied to the wires, the rat felt a mixture of pleasure, satisfaction, and bliss indescribable, akin to orgasm, but infinitely better. Then the wires were connected to a switch which the rat could activate directly. When released, the rat pecked at the switch at the rate of 8000 times an hour until it had to pause for food, and that pause was brief.

Dr. Leary described the pleasure of an LSD experience as the pleasure of a musician when he gets the whole works playing together in the same key, or the ecstasy that perhaps Einstein got when he worked out a formula, or the ecstasy that a mother feels at certain crucial times in child rearing. It is this sort of intense pleasure, incapable of being verbalized, which the drug provokes.

Are the hallucinogenic drugs a trigger to our pleasure center? Will we die, pecking at the button? Even here Leary has an answer. Suppose for a moment we are back in the year 1900. The automobile has just been invented. How do the people, the ultimate judges, look at this frightening monster?

> . . . First of all, we object to the dangers: high speeds will snap nervous minds, gas fumes are fatal, the noise will prevent cows from giving milk, horses will run away, criminals will exploit the automobile.
> . . . What can we do with speedy carriages? There are no

men to repair them. There are no roads, few bridges . . .
no skilled operators . . . Who will sell you gas?

. . . Perhaps they should be restricted to the government
elite, to the military, to the medical profession.

. . . Now consider consciousness-expanding drugs in 1963.
No language. No trained operators. Lots of blacksmiths
whose monopoly is threatened. A few people who do see
inevitable development of a new language, a transfigura-
tion of every one of our social forms. And these few, of
course, the ones who have taken the internal voyage.

. . . Be entertained by the social game you play. Remember, man's natural state is ecstatic wonder, ecstatic intuition, ecstatic accurate movement. Don't settle for less.

Throughout this chapter I have had to fight the tempta-
tion to editorialize. Dr. Leary's views are quite different
from mine. Huxley foresaw *Soma,* and is now making his
prophecy self-fulfilling, and Leary is his apostle. I personally don't want a brave new Soma-world, visited or revisited.
Yet I must admit that I have never expanded my consciousness artificially. To people who think the drug is dangerous,
Leary says:

These drugs are dangerous to several groups of people.
They're dangerous to anyone who has a vested interest in
any of our psychological or psychiatric or educational programs, because there's no question in our minds that we
open up new possibilities of learning without teachers, of
understanding your self without doctors, and of coming to
an awed and reverent understanding of life without a spirit-
ual guide or minister. Now this is going to play havoc with
lots of the games that are being played and lots of the control which is being exercised in our society.

It occurred to us very recently that these drugs cause temporary insanity and panic in certain classes of adminis-
trators and perhaps certain forms of psychiatrists, who have
not taken the drug, but there's very little panic being caused
in people who have had the experience. Listen to them . . .

# (5
# PANSPERMIA

A meteorite falls flaming through the atmosphere to hit the surface of the earth. Not an unusual event. But before 1800 nobody believed that stones could come out of the sky. The stories of falling stones were old wives' tales, told in furtive whispers by the superstitious, told about a vengeful God hurling missiles from heaven. In 1803 the French physicist Jean Biot observed a fall of stones himself. He reported his sighting to the French Academy, and since then, with official backing, falls have been observed regularly. It has been estimated that 300,000 tons of matter enter our atmosphere, and perhaps 1000 meteorites actually reach the surface of the earth every year. Yet, even today, mystery surrounds the origin and nature of meteorites.

Meteorites are either stony or metallic. Those of the stony variety are essentially rocks, composed mostly of silicates. The metallic meteorites are composed mostly of iron, with traces of nickel and other metals such as cobalt. Most of the stony meteorites contain stone droplets, chondrules, which are spread throughout the body. Their distribution is so uniform they resemble small pebbles in well-mixed concrete. They speak silently of homogenizing processes of formation we do not know on earth, and they speak of life, life somewhere out in space.

Another rare type of stony meteorite has been found: the carbonaceous chondrite. Only about seventeen stones of this type are known positively; six more possibly fit this category. These meteorites have a crumbly consistency, like a dark hard clump of dirt, and are encased in a fused shell which is formed by the heat generated during their flight through our atmosphere. These stones are rich in carbon compounds and contain substances that some scientists believe are the fossil remains of biological processes. If these scientists are right, we may have ancient samples of extraterrestrial life in our possession today. What are these bodies telling us? Where do they come from?

The first observed fall of a body of this type occurred in recent times on March 15, 1806, in Alais, France. It was about five-thirty in the afternoon. A father and his son working in the fields heard what they thought to be a cannon shot, then a thundering, and then a whine that sounded like "the spinning of a well hoist." They saw a body coming out of the sky toward them. It struck the earth. The object was a strange piece of black material, less than a foot in diameter, covered with a thin fused outer layer. It had a crumbly consistency and resembled nothing that was known to have come from the sky before.

The strange meteorite came to the attention of the prominent chemist Jacob Berzelius in 1834. After some hesitation he sensed that he had something new here, something important. He saw the apparent similarity between certain components in the meteorite and terrestrial organic substances. He asked the question, "Does this carbonaceous earthy material truly contain humus or a trace of other organic compounds? Does this possibly give a hint concerning the presence of organic structures in other planetary bodies?" This is the question that's still bothering scientists today. Since the time of Berzelius, analytical techniques have become immensely more precise and exact. These techniques have been brought to bear on the problem, yet they have not produced results which are convincing to all or even to most scientists.

The tests performed on these meteorites have been long and exhaustive. From Berzelius' first analysis, to the very delicate measurements being carried out across the world today, the preponderance of data indicates that indigenous organic matter does exist in these stones. The modern analytical techniques have included mass spectrographic methods which have indicated the presence of chemicals which would be expected if fossil biologic material were present; the infrared spectrograph has detected fatty acids; the various chromatographic analyses have confirmed the presence of different organic materials; optical activity measurements have been made, again with positive results; other chemical analyses have detected porphyrins, amino acids, and nucleic acid components. The bulk of the data speaks loudly for the conclusion that organic material is really present and that it came to earth within the meteorite.

But even with all of these data, most scientists are not certain that these meteorites really contain samples of extraterrestrial life. There is the spectre of earth contamination. A single fingerprint would provide enough organic material to upset the sensitive analytic measurements. Perhaps more importantly, there is a great deal of doubt about the validity of these data because these meteorites do not show the characteristics of sedimentary rocks that were deposited in water. On earth it is this type of rock which contains fossils. Water is necessary for the generation of life; if we believe that there are fossils in these meteorites, we have to suppose water existed on the body from which these meteorites came. Yet physical examination does not indicate that these meteorites were submerged for long periods of time. (Nevertheless there appears to be general agreement that water was present in some form on the parent body. This remarkable conclusion was reached in 1954, after the trapped water in a carbonaceus meteorite was found to have a deuterium-hydrogen ratio different from terrestrial water.)

Without free surface water, how can there be life? Without life, how can there be fossils? There follows then the implied question: Without assurance of water on the surface of the parent body, how can we believe the test data? This is a case of a missing hypothesis: since a mechanism for life formation without surface water cannot be described, the observed data are also questioned. This is analogous to the situation of ESP research in which controlled experimental tests produce data that cannot be explained by any plausible cause-effect relationship; therefore, the whole concept is questioned.

The modern controversy began in 1961, when Drs. Bartholomew Nagy, Warren Meinschein, and Douglas Hennessy presented a paper to the New York Academy of Sciences. These gentlemen had been conducting research into the organic chemistry of petroleum at Fordham University and the Esso Research Laboratories. Using roughly the same mass spectrometric techniques, they found that a sample from a carbonaceous meteorite contained materials similar to those found in terrestrial sedimentary rocks. To them it was certainly a straightforward finding. They reported it modestly in their paper, using the reserved tones and phrases of the profession:

> . . . it appears that biogenic processes occur and that living forms exist in regions of the universe beyond the earth.

They weren't prepared for the reaction their paper produced. The day after the meeting *The New York Times* reported:

> . . . A meteorite that fell in France a century ago, which has just been subjected to modern analysis, has been found to contain chemical compounds closely akin to the chemicals in the living processes of plants and animals on earth.
>
> One hydrocarbon found in the meteorite is a chemical cousin of a sex hormone. Another is a chemical cousin of cholesterol, the material that is believed to plug the arteries in heart attacks and strokes.
>
> Three scientists presented the evidence at the New York Academy of Sciences last and said:
>
> > "We believe that wherever this meteorite originated something lived."

This report stirred the pot. Dr. Nagy told me that he really wasn't as positive as the news article indicated and his conclusions had been exaggerated. He felt that, while his data indicated that life might have existed wherever the meteorite originated, much more work would have to be done before any firm conclusions could be reached. This is still his attitude. Nevertheless, his paper and the later news article brought segments of the scientific community to their collective feet. Meteorites simply have not shown evidence of originating from bodies with appreciable surface water; therefore, the previous conclusion had been that life was impossible on the meteorite's parent body. Now here was a brash young man, saying there was evidence of life in these stones. Perhaps he was just observing contamination which had been introduced since the meteorite fell. Maybe he was looking at his own fingerprints. Perhaps his positive results were only the markings of the wax crayon used at the museum. Maybe these chemicals he saw were spores breathed in by the meteorite as it passed from the vacuum of space into our pressurized atmosphere. Perhaps his laboratory techniques were inadequate.

Dr. Nagy told me the reaction was "a cry that the findings were impossible." One biochemist said, "I've been through this sort of thing myself, and I think someone ought to warn these young fellows that they're sticking their necks out. Unless they're pretty darn sure of their results they can ruin their careers with something as sensational as this."

The screams were to become even louder. Later in the year, during the summer of 1961, Dr. George Claus, a young microbiologist at the New York University Medical Center, visited Dr. Nagy's laboratory. He looked at some electron microscope photographs which enlarged the carbonaceous meteorite material 30,000 times, and saw something that resembled a diatom, a unicellular plant. It had an elongated central body and four flutes off to one side. Could this be the fossil which produced the hydrocarbons detected by Dr. Nagy's spectrographs? This was obviously an important question and it opened a whole new line of inquiry. The two scientists borrowed some fresh specimens of carbonaceous chondrites which had fallen in different parts of the world. They analyzed these carefully, studying the structure of each suspected fossil form they identified. In all, they found five distinct types of structures, similar in appearance to terrestrial algae which abound in any pool of stagnant water. But there were subtle differences in shape, and these differences made the scientists suspect that they had found fossils of extraterrestrial origin. These shapes generally had the appearance of biological organisms; they were composed of biological materials; they reacted to acids and stains in the same way as fossil terrestrial organisms; and they came from deep within the meteorite's interior.

Drs. Nagy and Claus published their work in the November 18, 1961 issue of the British magazine *Nature*. Their article, titled "A Microbiological Examination of Some Carbonaceous Chondrites," contained the guarded conclusion:

> . . . We are of the opinion that these observations suggest that the organized elements may be microfossils indigenous to the meteorite . . .

There it was. Not only did the meteorite samples contain hydrocarbons which pointed to life, they contained remnants of the life forms themselves. This really brought out the antagonists. The leader of the opposition was Professor Edward Anders of the Enrico Fermi Institute for Nuclear Studies at the University of Chicago. He and his associate Dr. Frank W. Fitch of the Department of Pathology tried to duplicate the microscopic forms detected by Nagy and Claus, using only terrestrial organisms. They did, in fact, prove fairly conclusively that one of the five types reported in the *Nature* article, was nothing more than a stained ragweed pollen. In reading their paper I was left with the feeling that they implied: if *one* of Nagy and Claus' molecules can be terrestrial, why not all? They said:

. . . This supports the previous contention that morphology
alone is not an adequate criterion for proving the extraterrestrial orig'n of suspected life forms in meteorites . . .
one person can be familiar with only a fraction of the
morphological diversity of plant spores. Even common pollen
grains may become so altered that they are unrecognizable
when treated in an unfamiliar way.

Prior to their ragweed explanation for one of the five shapes,
Drs. Anders and Fitch favored the view that the shapes
were produced by some inorganic process. Professor Anders,
at one time, said:

. . . in my opinion at least, the only connection between
meteorites and life is that an article on meteorites appeared
in a magazine called *Life*.

Papers and counterpapers, addenda and replies have been
sharply exchanged between the group led by Nagy and the
group led by by Anders. One writer called this dialogue a
"strange game of surrealistic tennis." Within the papers,
sometimes obliquely between the lines, sometimes blatantly
visible, are innuendos about carelessness, insufficient research, inadequate attention to detail.

Dr. Nagy's current work is being conducted at the University of California at San Diego under the auspices of
the National Aeronautics and Space Administration. He is
engaged in full-time research. Most of his equipment has
been provided by NASA and in his words "is among the
finest money can buy." His laboratories occupy four small
rooms on the fourth floor of the new, starkly modern physics
and chemistry building at the La Jolla campus. On the wall
of his clean laboratory hangs a maze of bottles, tubes, and
pipes for the extraction of samples from material under
analysis. It is meticulously, almost surgically clean. The
glass is cleaned in acid; every system under test is sealed

to prevent contamination. Dr. Nagy shows you the spec-
trometers, the polarimeters, the chromatographic plates
with unmistakable pride. Clearly this is his domain.

His accent retains a strong flavor of Hungarian. Even
without hearing his accent, one could guess his middle-
European origin simply from the way he holds a cigarette:
in the tips of his fingers rather than between them, and with
the lighted end pointed up. In the old country his father
was curator of the Hungarian National Museum. From this
scientific environment he came to the United States to take
his Master's Degree in mineralogy at Columbia University.
He took his doctorate in geochemistry at Penn State, and
after several years in research with Pan American Oil
and Cities Service in Tulsa, Oklahoma, he returned to Fordham University as Professor of Chemistry. Now, at 39, he is
working at La Jolla with Professor Harold C. Urey. He does
not teach; research fills his professional life completely. He
speaks softly, intently, and rapidly, often leaning forward
to emphasize a point. He is slim and his enthusiasm shows
in his dark eyes. Of this vigor, Dr. Urey has said:

> . . . They [Nagy, Claus, Meinschein, and Hennessy] are en-
> thusiastic, and if one is enthusiastic, one may make errors.
> On the other hand, one who is not enthusiastic will not be
> motivated to work.

All of the analyses made to date have sampled only that
portion of the organic material of the meteorites which is
soluble. Seven percent of the total weight of some carbonaceous chondrites is organic. Of this 7%, only approximately
5% can be extracted by solvents. Now, Dr. Nagy and his
associates are attacking the chemical analysis of the other
95% of the organic material. He feels that he has developed
methods for this new work, and if these are successful, he

may eventually produce more clues about the origin of the life forms in these mysterious rocks.

A meteorite is a stone that falls from heaven and strikes the earth. We say "falls from heaven" because we don't know where meteorites come from except from "up there somewhere." Most scientists believe that these bodies originate in the asteroid belt which lies roughly between the orbits of Mars and Jupiter. In this belt are tens of thousands of solar satellites, planetoids, ranging from the size of Ceres with a diameter of 480 miles to specks too small to be seen with a telescope. The combined mass of all the asteroids is small, about one-tenth that of the moon.

These pieces of matter may have once formed a planet. Bode's Law, which is an empirical statement of the distances between the planetary orbits and the sun, predicts that a planet should have revolved around the sun between the orbits of Mars and Jupiter. Only the asteroids are in this predicted orbit today. If a planet was once there, what could have happened to it? A very large amount of energy would have been required to make the missing planet fall apart. Neither volcanoes nor hydrogen bombs could theoretically account for this disintegration. Perhaps there was a cosmic encounter, a collision such as that suggested by Velikovsky, that blew the planet apart.

One school of thought holds that the asteroids are pieces of a planet that never formed because of the disturbing influence of the gravitational field of Jupiter. If this is true, we may be able to observe primordial matter in its natural state when the National Aeronautics and Space Administration sends a space probe to the asteroids.

An asteroid may become a meteorite when it is forced out of its normal orbit by a collision with another asteroid or the attraction of a nearby planet. This is a traditional view of the origin of meteorites but it is far from certain. First of all, there is a wide disparity in the age of meteorites. It is possible, through analysis, to determine the date of several key events in the life of a meteorite. Careful examination can provide us with the date when a meteorite, somewhere in space, changed from its molten state to a solid body. Typically this time is about 4.5 billion years ago, which tends to link the meteorite's parent body to the formation of the solar system since this is also the approximate age of the earth. Some meteorites, however, appear to have been molten as recently as 400 million years ago.

A meteorite, traveling through space, will be bombarded by cosmic rays which produce certain types of radioactive elements within the body. This bombardment will occur, of course, after the meteorite has been separated from its parent body and will last until it has passed through the earth's protecting atmosphere. By observing the magnitude of the cosmic-ray-produced radioactivity, the length of time that the meteorite remained in space can be estimated. Here the estimates vary widely: from 25,000 to one billion years.

Finally, the length of time since impact of the meteorite on the earth may be estimated by observing the extent to which the cosmic-ray induced radioactive material has decayed. We have not found any meteorites which struck the earth earlier than three million years ago. This in itself is strange since it is generally believed that falls have occurred since the earth was formed. The carbonaceous meteorites in our possession are very recent, and have all come from observed falls; these were collected within a few hours after their arrival.

So there are techniques available by which meteorites can be dated; we can tell when they were formed, how long they remained in space; we can tell when they hit the earth. But even with this data we cannot tell where or how the stones originated. At one time this was an interesting academic question; now that the possibility of life in meteorites has been proposed, the issue has become somewhat warmer. If life forms are in fact carried in these bodies, it may be very important to identify their source and nature. We will soon be sending men to the moon. Within thirty years our astronauts will be landing on other planets in our solar system. They will be looking for life or evidence of past life. In this search we must be absolutely certain of one thing —that the spacecraft and its explorers do not bring viable earth organisms with them. If this happened, detection of life on a new planet would be meaningless; it would give rise to speculation, conjecture, and debate that would make the arguments surrounding the carbonaceous chondrites seem like kindergarten. These meteorites may be telling us now, what kind of life to look for.

There is also the possibility that earth-life contamination on other planets will be damaging to the indigenous life forms. We have, after all, a rather disappointing history of bringing infectious diseases with us on our explorations. The meteorites could be telling us now whether our ecology will be compatible with the life we will find in space.

If we admit that earth-life forms may be dangerous to extraterrestrial life, extraterrestrial life may be dangerous to us. This is known as back contamination—the possibility that a returning spacecraft or astronaut will bring back an organism harmful to life on earth. It is by no means certain that this is a problem—biologists are divided on the issue, but clearly we should not trust to luck.

This problem was studied by a group of scientists during the summer of 1962. Their report states:

. . . The introduction into the earth's biosphere of the destructive alien organisms could be a disaster of enormous significance to mankind. We can conceive of no more tragically ironic consequences of our search for extraterrestrial life.

Several members of the Summer Study, as well as many of our colleagues in the scientific community, feel great concern over the possible consequences of back-contamination. On the other hand, some members consider the danger negligible.

Perhaps the meteorites could tell us now if there is danger. There is indeed reason to understand the origin of these bodies and the meaning of the organized elements which they contain.

Scientists solve puzzles and here is a puzzle of the most difficult sort: How can there be life forms in meteorites when these stones do not show a sedimentary origin? Some scientists, believing the analytic evidence for life in the carbonaceous meteorites, have tried to resolve this cosmo-biological conundrum. Dr. Urey has taken the experimental data at its face value and hypothesized a cosmos-information which could account for the fossils.

Dr. Urey believes that these fossil-bearing meteorites may come from the moon, and the fossils may be remnants of early life forms. One theory of the formation of the moon holds that the moon was captured by the earth. This may have occurred relatively recently; at a time when life was already present on earth. Other bodies may have been orbiting the earth when the moon was captured and the introduction of the moon into the system must have caused these bodies to change orbits. Some would have hit the earth, others the moon. These impacts must have occurred with tremendous force. On the moon they may have produced the maria. On the earth the collisions would have made great craters, or, if they occurred in the oceans, raised tremendous splashes of water. Dr. Urey computes that 200 or more objects of 100 km. or more in diameter could have hit the earth when the moon was captured; some of these hits would have been at low angles and would have driven earth materials out into space to great distances. Since life may have already been present on earth, the water splashes probably contained some simple life forms, or the water could have collected spores or organisms in the atmosphere as it splashed outward. Some of this material could have been captured by the moon where the water would have been soon lost, either by evaporation to space, or through seepage into the moon's crust. It is possible that the evolution of the entrained earth organisms continued on the moon's surface. In any event, in this hypothesis, the life forms in moon rock came from earth. Where do the meteorites come in? Suppose now that a large iron meteorite were to hit the moon. Bits of moon rock, containing the old earth life fossils would be kicked out into space. These secondary meteorites would coast in space on independent orbits until some, eventually, would collide with the earth. Dr. Urey believes it is these stones which we call the carbonaceous meteorites.

This idea can lead to other interesting speculations. Several scientists have suggested that water may exist on the moon in the form of subsurface glaciers. It is possible that primary life evolved in these glaciers and was then sent into space as a result of other impacts?

Could the carbonaceous meteorites come from Mars? Mars is large enough to hold surface water, even though our measurements from earth indicate that only very small amounts of water currently exist there. The temperatures and atmosphere of this planet are not so hostile that life on Mars can be ruled out; in fact, most exobiologists would probably indicate that the chances for discovering life on Mars are quite high. Carbon dioxide is the primary constituent of the Martian atmosphere.

Some astronomers have reported seasonal changes on the planet. When spring comes to a hemisphere on Mars, some observers report seeing a thin network of lines appear first near the polar caps, and then gradually spread toward the equator. The pattern repeats in the other hemisphere when the seasons reverse. The darkening apparently follows the thawing of the polar caps by fourteen to fifteen days, raising the speculation that what is actually being seen is vegetation growing next to natural "canals" or streams.

The astronomer W. M. Sinton spectrographically analyzed the light reflected from areas which he felt might contain vegetation. He found that the light reflected from the dark areas showed the presence of molecules containing carbon-hydrogen, the building blocks of organic matter. This work has been challenged quite recently, however. Two of the three peaks in the infrared spectrum which Dr. Sinton read as Martian hydrocarbons are now thought to arise from the earth's atmosphere. Nevertheless, one peak is still valid and serves as a possible indicator of organic material on Mars.

A very direct experiment has been performed by a group of scientists. They duplicated the probable atmosphere of Mars in the laboratory and tried to make elementary plants and animals live in this environment. They found that certain organisms could not only live in these conditions, but could reproduce and expand their colonies.

The whole nation watched as the Mariner IV probe passed near Mars in mid-1965 and transmitted the first close-up pictures of that planet back to earth. This *tour de force*

showed the most remarkable feature of the planet's surface
to be an occasional moon-like crater. These craters may
be the record of past meteorite impacts, collisions which
may have kicked off chunks of Martian sod and shot them
out into space billions of years ago. Is it possible that carbonaceous chondrites are pieces of this primordial soil?

The unweathered appearance of these craters suggests
that the surface of the planet is very old. Large bodies of
liquid water and dense atmosphere have probably not
been present on the planet for billions of years. The tenuous
Martian atmosphere does not filter ultraviolet radiation
well. All of these factors reduce the chances for life on that
planet. At a National Academy of Science meeting held in
October 1965 Dr. Philip H. Abelson, a very influential
scientist, editor of the respected magazine *Science,* said that
the lack of hydrogen in the atmosphere of Mars would
probably prevent the formation of organic matter such as
amino acids. If there were no amino acids, there would be
no life. Mariner IV has provided a glimpse into a strange
world. It has not added to the arguments for life on that
planet.

Dr. Brian Mason, curator of the American Museum of
Natural History, and Dr. Albert E. Ringwood of the Aus-
tralian National University believe that the carbonaceous
chondrites may originate neither in the asteroid belt nor
from the surface of a solar system body. They have inde-
pendently suggested that the meteorites may be remnants
of the cosmic dust that originally aggregated to form the
planets and satellites of the solar system, that these sod-
like rocks coalesced in various orbits around the sun and
drew into solid bodies. In other words, these meteorites are
"representative samples of the dust that made up much of
the primitive solar nebula." In this process of condensation,

embryo planets would have been heated and melted by radioactivity and shaped by their own gravity, changing physical and chemical form, until finally the bodies of the solar system emerged. In this concept, the hydrocarbons which Dr. Nagy and the other researchers have taken to be the results of primitive fossils would be no more or less than complex chemicals, produced by non-biologic means. The agglomeration of this material would place on the surface of earth and, in fact, every planet and satellite, chemically complex, proto-life substances, which could become simple living organisms under the right conditions. "Perhaps," Dr. Mason says, "the organic compounds of the carbonaceous chondrites hold the key to the origin of life on this planet."

Although most scientists believe that life originated spontaneously on earth some two and a half billion years ago, this is by no means the only theory of how life came to be. There is, of course, the religious tale of Adam and Eve, which in its ultimate extrapolation accepts the first two spiral halves of the DNA molecule as the progenitors of mankind. There is, too, the panspermia hypothesis which holds that living organisms travel across space. These organisms, floating by themselves, or carried on bits of matter, perhaps on meteorites, strike planets at random. By chance, some find hospitable environments and the colonization of a new planet begins. Konstantin E. Tsiolkovsky, the great Russian rocket theorist who died in 1935, felt that this colonization was the ultimate mission of advanced intelligent beings on other planets.

It is fascinating to speculate that life may have come to earth through seeding by another civilization. If we wanted to prove this hypothesis, we might begin by analyzing the material contained in meteorites which fall today on the

earth's surface. While some scientists such as Dr. Nagy believe they have found evidence of organic compounds and
fossils in these bodies, other scientists believe that they have
found, not the remnants of life, but viable organisms which
can be made to reproduce by careful laboratory culturing.
The discovery of dead organisms in meteorites might provide silent evidence of life off the earth; discovery of live
organisms could change our whole view, scientific and religious, of the way life came to earth.

Are there organisms that are living or can be brought
to life in the core of these meteorites? This is the question
that Dr. Frederick D. Sisler, microbiologist with the U.S.
Geological Survey, and Dr. Walter L. Newton, chief of the
germ-free laboratory at the National Institutes of Health,
attempted to answer. They worked with chunks of a stone
that had fallen in Murray, Kentucky, in 1950. This particular meteorite was denser than most, which, to a degree,
guarded against accidental contamination on earth.

Obviously this kind of experimentation required very intense precautions against contamination. The scientists first
sterilized the whole outer surface of the fragments using
intense ultraviolet radiation for half a day. This was followed by cleaning with a caustic solution to oxidize the surface organic matter and immersion in hydrogen peroxide.
The meteorite was then placed over an open flame and finally cleaned in a germicide. This, in theory, should have
removed any biological surface contamination.

The surgically-clean rocks were handled in the germ-free
tanks of the National Institutes of Health. These tanks are
stubby horizontal stainless steel cylinders, with heavy viewing portholes and built-in rubber gloves for handling the
sterile material within the tank. Germ-free animals, lacking
the usual parasitic flora and fauna of their atmospheric

counterparts, have lived their uncontaminated lives in the controlled environment of these tanks.

Drs. Sisler and Newton pulverized a few grams of the meteorite's central core within one of the clean tanks. They injected some of this dust into germ-free rats to provide a new host to any organisms in the dust. Another portion of the dust was placed in several different nutrient culture media within the tanks and incubated. After several months the fluid in the test tubes began to cloud, a white ring appeared; some reaction was taking place in the tubes. Samples were removed and examined under a phase-contrast microscope. There, in the field, were small particles, appearing "like sausages you might have twisted, thrown on the floor and jumped on," according to the scientists. They were the approximate size and shape of bacteria and unlike anything Dr. Sisler had seen in his years of study of terrestrial microorganisms. To scientific audiences Dr. Sisler described these particles as a helix cut into small pieces.

It would be easy to jump to conclusions with this kind of data at hand—conclusions that range from incompetent experimental procedures to panspermia. Do these strange microscopic bacteria come from earth after all? In an effort to find out Dr. Sisler took a similar chunk of meteorite and soaked it for several days in a broth containing a high concentration of terrestrial microorganisms. He was trying to soak them in—to purposely contaminate the meteorite's interior. After the soaking he cleaned the meteorite using the same process as before, ultraviolet radiation, hydrogen peroxide, and germicide. A portion of the fragment was then reduced to dust and cultured. None of the microorganisms present in the pre-test soak were found in the resulting broth. This strongly suggests that Dr. Sisler's sterilization procedures were effective in removing surface contamination, and the particles that reproduced within the culture were indigenous to the meteorite.

The word "life" includes many different processes; were these particles in the broth produced from the Murray meteorite really "living?" Drs. Sisler and Newton produced serial cultures from the first growth. The fact that both later cultures also grew shows that the particles, in fact, reproduced. To many this is "life."

To Dr. Sisler the results of these tests did not necessarily indicate that live organisms came to us from space. According to a report which he presented in 1961, Dr. Sisler believed that the inert organic matter in the chondrites may have been coaxed into life when they came in contact with the nutrient broth. These strange rod-like particles might have generated spontaneously.

Is it possible that these meteorites are the seeds of life on earth and elsewhere, and favorable, nutrient environments, spark these seeds to life?

Although Dr. Sisler's attitude has always been cautious, I asked Dr. Nagy how the scientific community responded to Dr. Sisler's work. His answer: "He was battered." Many scientists feel that inert bacteria, perhaps even protobacteria, could not survive, viable, after millions of years of exposure to the space environment. In space there are very low temperatures, absolute vacuum, ultraviolet radiation, solar proton winds.

Dr. Sisler today feels that the work of Dr. Philip H. Abelson, relating to the effects of radiation and extreme temperature on the survival of bacteria, presents perhaps the strongest evidence against the possibility of the extraterrestrial origin of the microorganisms isolated from meteorites.

Can there ever be absolute proof? Dr. Sisler has written me:

> . . . The question of origin of the organic matter and micro-
> organisms [in meteorites] still remains unsettled. As
> mentioned . . . I do not believe the controversy will be
> completely cleared up until source material is collected
> aseptically from outer space. The next best source might be
> specimens collected in Antarctica . . .

The space capture mission has already been discussed by
NASA scientists. Here an astronaut or unmanned automatic
station would collect meteoroids *in situ,* store them in sterile
containers and return them to earth for analysis. Carbonaceous chondrites will be required from these missions, and
because of their rarity, such a catch would be lucky indeed.
Perhaps this mission could be assigned to the crew of a
space station. Their extended time in orbit would greatly
improve chances for capture of the *avis obscura.*

Antarctica is mentioned as the second choice by Dr. Sisler
since the cold of that continent makes it much less likely
that terrestrial contamination will occur after impact. Scar-
city of population and relative infrequency of meteorite impacts at the earth's poles would certainly delay any active
implementation of this latter suggestion.

Dr. Nagy showed me a letter he wrote recently to one of
his antagonists. He said in part:

> . . . I am genuinely sorry that you decided against a joint
> effort to find out the reason of the differences . . . found
> by our two laboratories. Perhaps together we might have
> discovered the reason for these differences and arrived at
> some creative ideas and meaningful conclusions. I think you
> will agree with me that the exact nature of carbonaceous
> meteorites will not be known for many years to come and in
> the end what will count, and what will be remembered, is
> not the heated debate, but the scientific data which is cor-
> rect . . . In science, as in all scholarship, the quality of the

work and the idea is what really counts and not the individual. I believe in this principle.

The search and the debate will continue, but one day man will know the answer to the riddles described in this chapter; riddles about the origin of life, the nature of meteorites, and the nature of the sociology of science.

# (6
# WHO'S
# THERE?

Simply *knowing* that another intelligent race is out there, beyond our solar system somewhere, would have tremendous significance. As Copernicus moved the center of the universe from the earth to the heliocentric sun, so would the discovery of another intelligent race move the center of our self-concept from the selfish ego toward a philosophy in which man, earthman, would be part of a broader scheme. We would no longer be isolated giant molecular systems, scurrying, antlike, on an isolated celestial island. We would no longer be freaks of an accident of chemistry, reproducing through drives we do not understand, pushing toward unverbalized and indefinable goals in a maelstrom of unpurposeful continuity; suddenly man would be a member of the community of life.

If our contact with another race were to permit the exchange of information we might gain more than a new self-image: we might gain new knowledge directly. Such speculation is not merely idle conjecture; there are scientists who today are trying to design languages by which we might communicate with extraterrestrials. This commerce in ideas could raise us to levels of achievement many thousands of years beyond our present accomplishments. There is indeed a reason to ask if there is anyone else out there.

If our race wanted to contact other alien races how would we do it? First we might think of simply going to their planet in a space ship of some sort, if our propulsion systems were powerful enough and if we knew where to go. Or we might put up a beacon, visible to the universe, so that other races could observe it and know that there were other centers of intelligence in the heavens. Or, as a third possibility, we might try broadcasting radio signals to the universe so that any other race capable of hearing our signals, would know that we exist.

From the standpoint of sheer cost and technological complexity, the latter approach seems to be the one an advancing civilization might logically try first. We have been around as an organized civilization for only six or seven thousand years, yet our skill in radio communication has already evolved to the point where it is feasible to consider contacting alien societies by this means.

To communicate by radio takes fantastically small amounts of power. An amateur radio operator can send his signals around the world with less than five watts of power, under the proper conditions. The Mariner II space probe transmitted data from Venus, 54 million miles away, using a transmitter with only 3 watts of power. With antennas and transmitters available on earth today we could send signals out over ten light-years. At that distance our present-day receivers would be sensitive enough to detect the signal.

Is it inappropriate to assume that other societies, equal to or advanced beyond our own, would have developed similar concepts and recognized the potential in these techniques for interstellar communications?

So radio it is. If we want to listen for other signals, where do we point our antennas, and to what frequency should we tune our receivers? First of all, intelligent life almost certainly does not exist within our solar system. Mars and other planets may have life forms, but these probably will not be of the intelligent canal-digging variety. To find alien civilizations we must look beyond our solar system to dark planets circling distant stars. No astronomer has ever seen a planet outside of our solar system; we can see only the distant stars themselves. Yet it is quite probable that the cosmological accident that placed planets around our star, the sun, also occurred elsewhere in our galaxy and in other galaxies. Many astronomers feel that *all* single stars must have planetary systems. The number of stars is so great that even if the creation of a planetary system around a central star is a relatively infrequent phenomenon, planets must abound in the heavens.

Assuming then that other planetary systems exist, many questions still remain. How many of these planets can support life? Even if they are capable of supporting life, will simple life forms generate and will these evolve into intelligent societies? Even if intelligent societies emerge will they be communicative? Can societies survive their own propensity and capacity for self-destruction long enough to "get a message out?"

We must ask how long an alien technical society will be *capable* of transmitting. On earth about two and one half billion years elapsed from the appearance of the first cell to recognizable man. But how much longer will our evolution continue? We have now evolved to the point where we can cause our own destruction. We are in the age of overkill. Perhaps all societies reach this point as a consequence of their technical inventiveness. If societies generally progress to this point and kill themselves off, we have a chance of hearing only very young races before we meet the same fate. On the other hand, our society may last a very long time before it becomes extinct. If this is the model of evolving intelligence in the universe, we have more time; there will be more planets with life to listen to. Then the question becomes, Will we be listening when they are transmitting?

Consider that there may be some species that simply do not wish to communicate. For example, suppose some advanced alien societies resemble the dolphin. Some recent work by Dr. J. C. Lilly and others suggests that these animals can communicate with each other using sounds and a form of language. Certainly their order of intelligence is quite high. They apparently enjoy life, protect their young, move in cooperative schools; in short they have many attributes of a civilized species. If dolphinlike societies were to emerge on other planets and these were the norm, there would probably be no hope of contacting them via radio. If a war were to eradicate man, would the dolphin emerge, a million years hence, as the master of the earth's environment?

Nor is war the only means of potential destruction of a species which calls itself intelligent. We do not have full control over our environment. Smog may yet suffocate us. Some meteorologists have estimated this could happen within a hundred years. Population expansion could cause our race to lose interest in anything short of food production. Drugs, leisure, all of these may make the communicative period of our own society, and presumably an alien society, very short indeed.

These dangers notwithstanding, scientists, such as Dr. Frank Drake of Cornell University, have estimated that the communicative period of an intelligent civilization may last from a thousand to a million years. If the beginning of our own extraterrestrial communicative phase is dated to the early experiments of Maxwell, we have pressed the art for less than one hundred years. This factor, the length of time in which a society can and wishes to communicate, is a significant key in estimating how many alien groups we might have a chance of hearing.

All of these "if's" can be combined into a mathematical equation which leads to an estimate of the number of societies which at any instant of time may be in a position to communicate with other extraterrestrial societies. Dr. Drake estimates that between 1000 and 1,000,000 such societies may now exist, and that these are, on the average, 1000 light-years away.

If we were to hear signals from a society 1000 light-years away we would receive information which they transmitted 1000 years before, and if we were to answer, the total elapsed time would be 2000 years, the time between the birth of Christ and the present day. Thus any society which embarks on an interstellar communications experiment needs, in addition to its technological prowess, longevity and perseverance.

If we wanted to listen for these foreign races, what emission frequency would we choose? Various scientists have suggested gamma rays, infrared radiation, visible light, and microwaves. In selecting the most effective region to use we might logically look for a very prominent natural frequency, one which the scientists of other races might have found interesting too. For example, interstellar hydrogen has a natural spectral line at a wave length of 21 centimeters. This frequency appears to be invariant, and presumably early in the evolution of radio technology any intelligent species would have constructed equipment to detect this frequency. So here's a possible choice: we could set our equipment near this frequency in hopes that similar equipment would exist at the other end.

It was this type of reasoning that led Dr. Drake to propose Project Ozma, the earth's first serious attempt to listen for extraterrestrial radio signals. He aimed a very sensitive antenna and receiver at two stars close to the earth of the type which might have planetary systems: Tau Ceti and Epsilon Eridani. He listened for three months near the frequency of 21 centimeters. No signals were heard, but the project may have marked the beginning of a new scientific discipline, a new frontier.

In April 1958, Dr. Drake joined the staff of the National Radio Astronomy Observatory in Green Bank, West Virginia. The observatory was still under construction then. It was being built in the hilly West Virginia countryside, near the Virginia border, on a site particularly selected for its low level of radio noise. The Observatory is in Deer Creek Valley, surrounded by mountains rising to 4000 feet. These mountains shield the sensitive antennas from man-made radio transmissions. As one comes over the last hill, and looks down on the valley, he sees a mild green plain, spotted with trees, small buildings, and a water tower; the big parabolic dishes, turned impressively skyward, seem somehow discordant in this quiet place.

The Observatory had its beginning in 1954 when a group of American astronomers attending a Washington symposium on radio astronomy decided that progress in this field would require a cooperative effort, a pooling of resources that could bring the best minds and facilities together in one place in the United States. The National Science Foundation supported a feasibility study based on this suggestion and in 1956 a contract for construction and operation of the proposed observatory was let to the Associated Universities, Inc., a nonprofit organization formed to operate large scale research facilities for the academic community. Ground was broken in 1957 and the telescopes began operation in October 1958 under the direction of acting administrator Dr. Lloyd V. Berkner, an early radio pioneer.

Radio astronomy is a relatively new astronomical technique. As a scientific discipline it dates back to 1931 when an engineer for the Bell Telephone Laboratories, Karl G. Jansky, pointed a high gain antenna toward the sky in an effort to find the source of high frequency static which was interfering with his company's radio traffic. He found several sources: lightning and man-made interference were there, of course, but there was something else, a new source, that stayed fixed with respect to the stars. It seemed to be coming from beyond our earth, from beyond our solar system. He reported his results at a symposium in 1933. While some newspapers picked up the story, the reception accorded him by most of his fellow astronomers was only a slightly disinterested ho-hum. Dr. Fred Whipple and other young Harvard astronomers were among those who offered Jansky encouragement.

Grote Reber, a Chicago radio amateur operator, followed Jansky's report and saw its significance. Being an amateur astronomer, too, Reber combined his hobbies and built a large parabolic antenna dish and pointed it at the sky to find and track the noise Jansky had reported. As a nonprofessional he had no reputation at stake. Since I am a ham, too, I can almost feel part of his excitement as he aimed his home-made big dish at the stars and started mapping the noise that came from parts of the sky where there were no visible stars. (For the benefit of fellow hams: His XYL probably said, "You're not going to put that ugly thing up in the back yard, are you?") With the publication of his results, radio astronomy had started.

(Occasionally, even in this day of highly tuned multi-million dollar facilities, run by highly tuned specialists, an amateur can through accident or design find a niche for contribution, through patient experimentation or insightful genius. These nonprofessional savants may presage the pattern of our automated future when creative science-hobbying can provide the intellectual stimulation of an otherwise vacant, idle leisure.)

This is the job of the National Observatory: to scan and map the heavens using sensitive and directional radio antennas and receivers, to look for sources of radio energy which may or may not correspond to the sources of visible light we call stars. Radio astronomy has opened a new window looking out from earth; the data which can now be collected are no longer limited by the sensitivity and bandwidth of human eyes or photographic plates, but only by electronic equipment and our shielding atmosphere.

Dr. Drake saw other potentialities in this equipment. Early in 1959 he suggested to Dr. Berkner that the 85 foot dish at Green Bank be pointed toward stars likely to have planets, to listen for signs of their life. Dr. Berkner was interested. He was a man of great vision.

In April 1959 Dr. Drake's plan was accepted by Dr. Otto Struve, the new director of the observatory. The two astronomers had agreed to withhold publication of their decision and to proceed with this project confidentially, because they felt its potentially sensational nature might cause unwarranted excitement, and perhaps stir up the opposition unnecessarily.

Coincidence is not rare in scientific invention. While Dr. Drake was making his proposal at Green Bank, physicists Drs. Giuseppe Cocconi and Phillip Morrison of Cornell were also considering methods by which an alien society might contact us. Cocconi hypothesized that gamma ray communication might be the mode that an extraterrestrial race might select for communication. He wrote to Sir Bernard Lovell, director of the world's largest radiotelescope at Jodrell Bank, England, in June 1959, and asked him if he would undertake such a search for intelligent sources of radio or gamma rays. Dr. Lovell's reply, a month later, not surprisingly, was negative. There was more pressing business for Jodrell Bank.

In August 1959 Cocconi and Morrison suggested that the 21 centimeter band, the resonant line of hydrogen in free space, might be a good place to begin the search since any intelligent physicist, be he an earthman or not, would surely have observed this line and noted its significance. Their proposal was published in *Nature*, September 19, 1959. Although Dr. Drake's identical plan was already being implemented at Green Bank, Cocconi and Morrison published first; they had *priority*, that most elusive scientific commodity.

After the Cocconi-Morrison article appeared in *Nature*, however, the Green Bank scientists made their project public. The effect of this publication, stating that a project was in being, was electric; the Establishment split; some brayed and some applauded.

At four A.M. on April 8, 1960, Project Ozma was started;

the dish was pointed toward Tau Ceti. The operators must have felt a great sense of insignificance. They were literally calling out to a race that might not exist on a planet that might not exist. They were saying, "Come in please," using a technology that might be unique to earth.

They heard no signals. Not surprising. Dr. Drake then switched to the other star, Epsilon Eridani.

*Signals.*

*Signals.*

Loud periodic signals. Unmistakable. Before any checks could be run on the authenticity of their extraterrestrial origin, they went off the air.

The patient scanning continued. The possible detection was kept secret, while Dr. Drake sought to find out if it really came from Epsilon Eridani. Some weeks later, after many repetitions of the strange signal, it was identified as man-made, and of terrestrial origin.

The search was concluded at the end of July 1960, when more pressing work demanded its abandonment. The receivers had been on for 150 hours, an infinitesimally short period. Nothing had been proven or disproven. One rational technique for detecting other communicative intelligence had been attempted for but an instant.

Dr. Struve, director of the project and a very respected astronomer, wrote an article relating to the reception by the community to the project. It was titled *Astronomers in Turmoil.* He said that Ozma had been given an "unreasonable amount of publicity, often incorrect or distorted and always with the wrong emphasis." The emphasis was always strange little green men from outer space rather than the meaningful derivatives of the work. Since the stars being surveyed were necessarily close to earth, the probability of finding life was almost zero from the start, and the astronomers participating in the experiment knew it. Why then did they proceed? Because Ozma would give experience in receiver design, and in observational techniques. And there was always just a bare chance that something would be heard. Dr. Struve said:

> . . . (Ozma) has aroused more vitriolic criticisms and more laudatory comments than any other recent astronomical venture, and it has divided the astronomers into two camps: those who are all for it and those who regard it as the worst evil of our generation. There are those who pity us for the publicity we have received and those who accuse us of having invented the project for the sake of publicity . . . I can only describe as shameful any thought that we ourselves are seeking publicity . . .

I asked Dr. Drake about his impression of the reception given Ozma. He said that the attitude was "mostly positive, but some negative comments" were voiced. Why didn't a project of such scope and imagination run into trouble? Dr. Drake told me that this was probably because "the total cost of the project was extremely small, and so there could be no controversy raised over the question of whether substantial research funds were being properly used." Of the project itself, Dr. Drake said:

> . . . Project Ozma was indeed limited, because of lack of sponsorship, and particularly lack of antenna and personnel time with which to carry out the project. It was too early, but in fact the search should only have been continued with much more efficient equipment than was used in the original attempt . . .

The failure to detect signals at the instant of time during which we were listening shows that possible societies on the suspected planets of two stars were not transmitting, many years before, on 21 centimeters. Success would have meant a fantastically lucky combination of a large number of almost imponderable factors. Yet some scientists wonder if the failure wasn't significant in itself. They say that if intelligent life is indeed prolific in the universe, we should hear something once in a while, if not in Ozma, then in the course of our radio astronomy work. But we have heard nothing. What does this mean—uncommunicative civilizations? Perhaps. No planets? Short-lived, self-destructive civilizations? Perhaps there is no life off earth and our efforts point only toward utter, final disappointment and despairing isolation.

Dr. Drake is a youthful scientist with an easy broad grin. He wears open sport shirts, glasses with light rims, and has prematurely graying hair with a cowlick; in short he is an attractive, relaxed unassuming young man. He was born in 1932, a Midwestern Baptist. His father was a chemical engineer in Chicago and as a result, young Frank received an early scientific orientation. He was a good student in high school, and took his undergraduate work in physics at Cornell. After a stint in the Navy, where he specialized in electronics, he returned to Harvard to take his Ph.D. in astronomy. There he met and was taught and molded into a scientist by Dr. Bart J. Bok, Dr. Thomas Gold, and Dr. Cecelia Payne-Gaposchkin, who incidentally was one of the most outspoken anti-Velikovsky protagonists.

Clearly, Frank Drake is not typical of other innovators described in this book. Most scientists would not quarrel with the concept that life may exist on other galaxies, although many would argue that proving this isn't worth the time it will consume. Why then is this episode included? The belief that this proposition, that life exists on other galaxies, is amenable to scientific proof is very recent. Sci-

entists generally exclude from their research, problems which
have little chance of solution. Here is a new emerging field.
It is not in conflict with a background of data and hypotheses because the discipline is only now crystallizing. We
can watch its tenets form; watch it articulate admissible
subproblems; see its journals, symposia, and its university
chairs being created. We are present at the birth of exobiology which will derive its strength from the technology of
rocketry, biology and microbiology, communications, electronics, astronomy, astrophysics, and all these specialties related to the spectrum of skills called space sciences.

Now Dr. Drake's field is radio astronomy, a new discipline
itself, which should therefore be immune to the idea-chan-
neling power structure which can form in older fields of
scientific inquiry. We have certainly seen the hierarchy of
concept displayed in almost all of the essays of this book—
the power of the pronouncements of the senior scientist,
those ultimate "truths." Inevitably a younger man with
fresher ideas brings with him a young following and unseats
the old king to start the progress cycle again. Thus, science
progresses, not only in ideas but in personalities. The game
of science is a game of personality cult and for good reason.
A scientist makes his mark by his reputation—and nothing
is more personal than reputation. Radio astronomy is a
young discipline which therefore affords an opportunity to
observe the power elite forming. Of this struggle, Dr. Drake
has said:

> . . . We have seen in American radio astronomy an atti-
> tude of *laissez faire* among the younger scientists, which has
> resulted in many cases in uncontrolled competition, person-
> ality clashes, and controversies. Because of this rivalry,
> people have had to be very cautious in what they did be-
> cause they never knew from what direction a knife might

fly. In the long run, this has impeded the progress of American radio astronomy.

This has been dismaying to many of us and certainly unpleasant for those who have been the victims. But we see indications as time goes on of a growing maturity within the field. It will gradually acquire a coterie of elder statesmen, who can clamp the lid on situations before they do become harmful . . .

In reading this statement and in reviewing Dr. Drake's startling career, one cannot help but feel that Dr. Drake himself is an elder statesman-in-the-making and before too many more years have passed, radio astronomy and exobiology too will have become disciplines with elites, power structures and inviolate pre-established hypotheses.

Even while the experiments were going on at the observatory, other suggestions were being made about the methods an advanced civilization might choose to indicate its presence. Dr. Freeman Dyson of the Institute for Advanced Study at Princeton, New Jersey, wrote an article about the ultimate form of a hypothetical advanced civilization. Assuming that it is characteristic for the population of a planet to outstrip its available food supply à la Malthus, an advanced technological society would find ways to increase the surface available for food production and living space. This could be accomplished, he reasoned, by building a hollow sphere around the central sun out of the materials of the system's planets. The inner surface of this thin shell would be illuminated everywhere by its sun; almost total power from the star would become usable. To test whether such structures have been built, Dr. Dyson suggested that we scan the heavens looking for point sources of infrared radiation which would leak through such a shell.

This bold suggestion brought some stringent letters in

reply. The most telling was a letter pointing out that a shell such as the one Dr. Dyson suggested would collapse because of the gravitational stresses exerted by the central sun. This led Dyson, in a later letter, to picture a shell formed of a swarm of individual bits of matter, each in independent orbit, balanced by a combination of gravity, centrifugal force, and radiation pressure. This model is rather unsatisfying because these bits of matter would surely collide with rather disastrous results.

As dissatisfying as the concept may appear, certain Russian astronomers apparently picked up the idea and developed it further. They reasoned that an advanced society living on a shell surrounding a central sun would be able to stabilize the shell somehow. This society would then have tremendous amounts of energy available. This energy could be used to power a very large radio beacon at almost any frequency. They pictured a civilization developing in three phases. The earth is a type one society, relatively crude, taking the energy from its star in inefficient ways, using only that small portion of sunlight which falls naturally on its surface. A type two civilization might have restructured its solar system so that the entire star is surrounded as suggested by Dr. Dyson. Beyond this, they pictured the type three society developing to the point where a whole galaxy could be captured, maneuvered and finally encapsulated; a billion stars to serve their masters.

In 1964, the Russian astronomer Nikolai S. Kardashev, writing in *Astronomical Journal of the Soviet Academy of Sciences,* announced that he had found periodic radio signals emanating from two powerful radio stars, CTA-21 and CTA-102, and that these signals might be coming from an intelligent supercivilization. The frequency of these signals was 900 megacycles, a frequency particularly effective in long-range transmission. The stars were radiating a tremendous amount of energy. Usually radio sources seem to come from broad segments of the sky; these were point sources. The signals were periodic, each cycle lasting about a hundred days. Dr. Kardashev hypothesized that this great amount of power was coming from a type two civilization which had captured its star. The Russian reasoned that the energy of the star could have been powering a beacon that could be seen and heard across the galaxies. He thought he had found such beacons in CTA-21 and CTA-102.

On April 13, 1965, *Tass* interviewed the astronomers of the Moscow Astronomical Institute. Their report said that the signal came from, "intelligent beings belonging to a highly developed civilization," and that the signals were of "artificial origin, designed by reasonable beings."

The story broke across the front pages of the world. Walter Sullivan said in *The New York Times:*

> . . . If signals from another world have been intercepted, as suggested by a Soviet astronomer, it could prove to be the most revolutionary event in human history. That this has taken place, however, is far from certain.

Scientists were officially skeptical. "No observational evidence." "Not by any means conclusive." "Wait for further evidence." "Doesn't really hold water." Disbelief was general.

The Russians were not reporting a new body in the heavens. CTA-102 was a known radio and light source. In fact, its designation signifies that it was the 102nd radio source placed on Cal Tech's list A. It had been catalogued as a radio source by Dr. John Wyndham of Cal Tech's Owens Valley Radio Observatory and as a fluctuating light source by Dr. Allan Sandage of Mount Wilson and Palomar

Observatories. It is believed to be a quasar, a tremendously brilliant and distant point of radiating energy, probably resulting from an explosion of some sort, perhaps from the interaction of matter and antimatter. While variations in light intensity had been noted before, the discoverers of CTA-102 had not noted any variations in its radio strength. This observation was the claimed contribution of the Russians. Whether this implied that a supercivilization was transmitting was an entirely different matter.

The next day the story changed. The Moscow Astronomical Institute called a news conference on short notice. Officials of the Cultural Committee of the Soviet Government called correspondents to the Institute to provide them a "scientific explanation." The scientists there, including Kardashev and the directors of the Institute, said that it was impossible to tell if the signals had come from natural or artificial sources, and strongly implied that the confusion had come from overeager distortion by *Tass*. Professor Shklovsky said: "You know what the press does . . . Scientists could not tell *Tass* what to publish. It is our right to ask journalists that they respect their great responsibilities, which does not always happen." This was apparently a rare public slap at the official news agency. The Russian scientists asked astronomers in other countries of the world to aid them in listening to CTA-102 in order to identify the true origin of the fluctuating signals. These could result not only from advanced civilizations, the Russians said, but from a rotating star with a "very brilliant spot" or periodic occultation of the star by a planet.

It is worth repeating one specific question asked at this news conference and the answer it received. The reporter representing the *Los Angeles Times* asked, "Would any astronomer on the platform who believes the radio emis-

sions came from another civilization, please raise his hand."
Nobody on the panel raised his hand. Smiling, Professor
Shklovsky came forward and said that they were not going
to vote on a scientific matter. While there had been a time
when scientific truths had been determined by vote in the
Soviet Union, he said, those days were past.

Most scientists would agree that scientific "truths" cannot
be determined by vote. Yet consensus is intrinsic to the
scientific method. This consensus provides continuity to
the disciplines; it forms a point of departure for normal
research. Scientists first learn these positions of agreement
from textbooks, and later from technical publications and
symposia. Contributions to the state of the art are usually
made in small bits which gradually shape the consensus into
new articulations and specializations of the old ideas. When
new ideas run counter to the consensus, conflict, sometimes
violent conflict, results. This meeting in Moscow was, after
all, a statement that consensus still prevailed on the subject
of CTA-102.

Why had *Tass* been chosen for the original announcement? We have already seen that popularization before
scientific publication can often intensify controversy. Why
didn't the Russian astronomers publish in one of their technical journals first? I can think of three possible reasons.
First, in Russia there is a propensity to use scientific achievements for political fodder to help demonstrate to the world
a credible technological edge which yields political advantage. A popular announcement would tend to intensify the
political impact of a sensational discovery. Second, at the
time of the announcement, an intense funding battle was
occurring in the Presidium of the Academy of Sciences, according to *Vestnik*, its official organ, between astronomers
and nuclear physicists. Each discipline had been trying to

convince the Academy's planners that its segment deserved investment in new facilities; the astronomers wanted new radio telescopes and the physicists wanted new accelerators. It is possible that the announcement was timed and arranged by the astronomers to emphasize the value of astronomical discoveries to the scientific stature of the country. A little gamesmanship, perhaps. Third, I might suggest that the Russians believed what they said, but the weight of world opinion and perhaps government pressure forced them to reverse their position and *Tass* took the beating. Who knows?

A reporter put one last question to Kardashev as he left the meeting room: Did he really believe that life existed on CTA-102, that the radio emissions came from another civilization?

"I would like to believe it," he said. I wasn't there, but I imagine that he felt a little like Galileo after the Inquisition, when he muttered quietly, as the story goes, "But it does move."

This Russian episode illustrates one potential deficiency of the Ozma approach: when we find something we may not believe it.

Our technology is proceeding at such a rapid pace that what we consider the obvious means of communication today may be outmoded tomorrow. For example, the advent of superpowerful lasers may give rise to a whole new technology of communication. The work done in radio may be simply a precursor to the development of techniques necessary to the use of light, which after all is merely extremely high frequency electromagnetic waves. For example, can we picture a satellite orbiting beyond Jupiter, directing its powerful light beam outward to identify to any extraterrestrial observers that intelligent life exists near the sun? It would be powered by a long-life nuclear-electric system, and keyed to send a signal of unmistakably non-natural origin. Certainly we must admit that such a system may be feasible in a hundred years.

Dr. Drake and E. M. Purcell have suggested that advanced races may set up another type of beacon by modulating their central sun to make it stand out against the background of stars. By surrounding a star with a partially transmitting material, an alien race might be able to make us recognize the unnatural hand of intelligence in some remote corner of the universe. If the modulating material surrounding the star were, for example, a short-lived isotope, we might guess that the source was of intelligent origin since its continued presence would indicate that the filter was being replaced continually. However, I suspect that the astronomer who first observes this unnatural line on his spectrograph, will go to great lengths to reach some other conclusion. The first man to make this observation and publish an extraterrestrial life explanation will almost certainly face the derision of his fellow scientists.

Our rapidly developing technology even hints that direct travel to other sites of civilization might be possible someday. This is an exceedingly difficult problem. Today our rockets are probing the solar system, where we will almost certainly find some forms of life, but not intelligent forms. To go beyond the solar system requires propulsion of forms that can barely be verbalized today. Even at the speed of light, the average travel time necessary to reach a planet with a communicative society might be 1000 earth-years, one way. But near the speed of light strange things begin to happen to time. From Einstein's relativistic theories, we can predict that a vehicle moving at speeds significantly close to that of light, 186,000 miles per second, will have a time base that appears to be slow to an observer on the earth. A man on the spacecraft will not sense the slowing; his watch will seem to be running at the same rate. But an observer on the earth would see the traveler's watch running slow. The faster the spacecraft moves, the slower the watch would seem. The effect is not only an illusion, it is probably real biologically; the man on the spacecraft would be aging very slowly in comparison to the man on earth. Dr. Sebastian von Hoerner, a Green Bank associate of Dr. Drake's, ran some computations on a theoretical high speed trip to the stars. He assumed that the spaceship accelerated at one g, the acceleration of a body falling to the earth's surface. We are, of course, acclimated to this acceleration since we endure it each day. The spaceship ride would seem very smooth indeed. The velocity of the ship would increase 32 feet per second every second. In a year it would be traveling near the speed of light. If the propulsion system continued providing thrust, the ship's speed would continue to increase, gradually approaching the speed of light. To an earthman, the ship's time would seem slower and slower.

If a round-trip journey were completed in twenty years by the spaceship clock, the travelers would arrive back at the earth 270 years after they left, by earth time. If the trip took sixty years by the spaceship clock, almost 5,000,000 years would have passed on earth by the time they returned.

The problem is that we can't just yet build a spaceship that will accelerate with one g for periods of as long as a year. In fact, our most powerful rocket, the Saturn V, will hit peak accelerations of about 8 g's but its burning time will be limited to twenty minutes. This rocket is a tremendous vehicle, standing 350 feet tall and weighing 7,000,000 pounds at lift-off. Yet it does not pack enough energy in its cryogenic propellents to even approach the impulse required for the journey to the stars. Some other form of propulsion is needed, perhaps some form that derives its energy from the environment of space through which it travels. The space hydrogen ram-jet is one approach which has been suggested. This vehicle would scoop in interstellar hydrogen to be heated and accelerated by a nuclear reactor. But other scientists have pointed out that the scoops would have to be tremendous. Perhaps the scoops could be electromagnetic so that the fields of force from the spacecraft would induce the gas to flow into its burners. Another serious problem of high-speed interstellar travel has been pointed out: radioactivity would result from the impact of interstellar particles with the high-speed ship. These atomic bullets would strike the skin of the ship and penetrate into the nuclei of the atoms making up the metal of the ship's hull. This would activate the skin, making it radioactively hot, beyond the level that its occupants could endure. Again the answer might be an electrostatic or magnetic envelope around the ship which would deflect any approaching charged particles. Perhaps the field would deflect the particles into the ship's electromagnetic scoop to further augment its impulse.

In an earlier book I said that the search is on to find the secret of antigravity, which may ultimately prove to be more than a science fiction answer to travel to the stars. Gravity is a result of existing in our continuum. By virtue of the curvature of space, all bodies in space are accelerating. Gravitation can be compared to an inertial force resisting this acceleration. How then can the force resisting this indigenous acceleration be removed? There would appear to be three answers: reduce the gravitational mass to zero; reduce the acceleration acting on the mass to zero; or develop a force equal and opposite to the gravitational force. Satellites in orbit around the earth develop this third kind of force; their curved path produces a centrifugal acceleration which just balances the attraction of the earth's gravity. Hence they remain balanced in weightless orbits. Note that this is not antigravity in the sense that gravity has been eliminated, but rather a straightforward Newtonian balancing of forces. Similarly the chemical energy of rocket propellents produces a force which exceeds the gravitation attraction on the mass of the rocket. In this sense, antigravity may be possible. The breakthrough required is the development of a device which will produce thrust at least equal to its weight over very long periods of time. With such a device we could roam over the world, the solar system, and perhaps the universe, at our leisure. This is the problem space scientists will tackle in earnest in the next century.

Rand Corporation, in Santa Monica, California, recently conducted a long-range forecasting study. One aspect of the study was the prediction by panels of experts of possible scientific breakthroughs in the next fifty years. The median of opinion of these experts placed antigravity on the schedule shortly after the turn of the next century.

Some scientists believe that antimatter may have, as one of its properties, antigravity. A positron is a particle which has the mass of an electron, but a positive rather than a negative charge. When this particle was discovered, experimenters asked almost immediately whether other antiparticles such as antiprotons and antineutrons could exist. Continued research in the field of particle physics has, in fact, discovered such particles. On August 15, 1963, the Atomic Energy Commission announced that a Yale-Brookhaven team of scientists had found the last particle of antimatter, the anti-xi-zero. With this discovery there could be little doubt that a family of matter could be constructed with each portion of its atomic make-up bearing properties exactly opposite to matter as we know it. Drs. Fred Hoyle and Geoffrey Burbidge have speculated that entire galaxies outside of our own may be made up of antimatter and that at least some of the strong radio signals we receive from distant galaxies may arise from the collision of matter with antimatter. These scientists have speculated about the gravitational characteristics of antimatter:

> . . . It appears that the only way (matter and antimatter) could be so separated is by a gravitational force of repulsion between atoms and anti-atoms—in short, by antigravity, as opposed to the gravitational attraction that operates between atom and atom of ordinary matter.
>
> . . . the idea of antigravity cannot be accepted without destroying basic principles of the general theory of relativity. The successes of the relativity theory are so great that most scientists are not prepared at the present time to consider with equanimity the very considerable upheaval that would come about if it had to be abandoned or drastically modified.
>
> Experiments designed to look for the existence of antigravity are possible in principle and may be worth doing. One obvious test would be to generate a beam of antiprotons in an accelerator and project it over a path parallel to the earth to see whether it would rise or fall; if the beam rose, it would indicate that antigravity was operating.

There is perhaps more work going on in this field now than meets the eye. In 1956 *Inter-Avia,* a reputable international aviation and aerospace magazine, published an article entitled: "Towards Flight without Stress or Strain or Weight." The article was written by an American journalist "having close connections with scientific circles in the United States." It stated that gravity research projects were under way in every major country of the world. These projects were purported to be analytic as well as experimental. The experimental projects had supposedly reached the point where weight reductions of as much as 30% were demonstrated. On this issue we must remain skeptical; the article was unsigned and the techniques used to obtain this weight reduction were not described because of "security." The author either had a fantastic lead on the science story of the decade or he was simply extrapolating half-understood interviews.

Yet there are undeniable anomalies in our understanding of the functioning of gravity. Gravitational forces appear to propagate instantaneously; other forces take time to be transmitted. Certain stars appear to be drifting apart, falling outside of the general pattern of motion of the background of stars. Some scientists have detected anomalies in the motions of pendulums.

Antigravity is an unpopular scientific subject. If you doubt this, ask a physicist about it. Nevertheless, it may be possible. It may be the way to go to the stars.

Assume for the moment that one of the advanced civilizations we are trying to contact has solved this problem of space flight. Suppose they can travel from the stars. Have they visited us already? Dr. Drake has suggested that this idea not be rejected without consideration and Dr. Sagan has studied our mythology for evidence of stories relating to interstellar visitors. There are, of course, repetitive themes which can be interpreted in this light. Where did the concept of the devil come from? Or angels for that matter? Were they visitors stepping out of some ancient (to us) spaceship?

For example, the Bible itself has a passage which would be worthy of any modern science fiction writer describing a spaceship landing. It comes from the Book of Ezekiel:

> . . . And I began to see, and, look! there was a tempestu-
> ous wind coming from the North, a great cloud mass and
> quivering fire, and it had a brightness all around, and out of
> the midst of it there was something like the look of elec-
> trum, out of the midst of the fire.
>
> And out of the midst of it there was the likeness of four
> living creatures, and this was how they looked: they had
> the likeness of earthling man.
>
> And (each) one had four faces, and (each) one of them four
> wings.
>
> And their feet were straight feet, and the sole of their feet
> was like the sole of a foot of a calf; and they were gleaming
> as with the glow of burnished copper . . .
>
> . . . there was one wheel on the earth beside the living
> creatures, by the four faces of each.
>
> As for the appearance of the wheels and their structure, it
> was like the glow of chrysolite . . .
>
> And as for their rims, they had such a height that they
> caused fearfulness; and their rims were full of eyes all
> around the four of them.
>
> And when the living creatures went the wheels would go
> beside them; and when the living creatures were lifted up
> from the earth, the wheels would be lifted up.

And the passage continues, describing the sound of the craft
when it left, and its glow, and the instructions which came
from a voice which radiated from a sapphire-like structure
over their heads. Ezekiel was supposed to have been a
priest and a writer, an aristocrat who lived about 600 B.C.
Whatever else he was, could he also have been a reporter?

Could these travelers have placed a man on earth, a man
to leave his mark for future generations, to leave his mark
in such a way that future generations could not doubt that
he had possessed knowledge which marked him as a trav-

eler from another civilization? Don't scoff yet, please. I have no doubt that the great English satirist Jonathan Swift was born on earth, but let me use his *Gulliver's Travels, A Voyage to Laputa,* as an example. In this famous satire, published in 1726, he said that the planet Mars had two satellites orbiting in periods of 10 and 21.5 hours. Such satellites were unknown in his day of course, but in 1877, two satellites of Mars were found and their periods are 7.6 and 30.4 hours.

Swift said these bodies revolved around their mother planet at distances of three and five times the planet's diameter; the satellites actually orbit at distances of 1.4 and 3.54 times the diameter. These inaccuracies alone would have been enough to disqualify Swift as an extraterrestrial visitor, but the point is clear; A visitor might leave a record of his presence in our literature, to be discovered later by perhaps more intelligent men. And incidentally, the orbital periods and altitudes predicted by Swift were quite surprising; they represented bodies in rapid rotation, close to the planet. No other satellites with those characteristics were known at that time or now.

Perhaps the writings left for us by this hypothetical visitor are in the form of instructions or advice. The visitor might have wished to leave some of their advanced knowledge for us to ponder, and to guide us to broader and more significant achievements. The ancient writings which led to the Bible, for example, might be such documents.

Now to return for a moment to the satellites of Mars. These are very peculiar objects. They are less than ten miles in diameter. The Russian astronomer Shklovsky guessed that some anomalies in the orbit of Phobos, the closer satellite, might be explained if it were assumed that the satellite were hollow; that is, artificial. His publications on this subject were sensationally reported by the press. Shklovsky hypothesized that at some time past, residents of Mars launched these satellites into orbit to provide a refuge for themselves when their planet's atmospheric oxygen and surface water began to diffuse. This is a difficult hypothesis to accept since it is so unlikely that intelligent beings inhabit Mars. Suppose for a moment though that a visiting race wanted to leave a marker for us to discover after our civilization had advanced a little more. Would there be a better calling card than two artificial satellites around Mars?

Dr. Drake points out that there are many other possibilities, in fact so many that no type of organized search for artifacts can now be contemplated. As we proceed with the business of understanding history through archaeology, ancient literature, and space research, we must remain alert to this most unique potential discovery. But what would we say if a professor, digging in an ancient Samarian city, were to announce that a certain jug or shard came from outer space? I suspect our reaction would be anything but polite.

(7

# THE
# POWERS
# OF
# PRAYER

In a small darkened room the group was chanting over the seeds. They were praying to their god-figure that these small corn seeds might grow and give abundant fruit. This was their sacred fertility rite.

The room was cold and barren of furnishings. The group numbered perhaps ten men and women. They sat cross-legged on the floor, the seeds spread out in front of them. The earth in which the corn seeds would be planted was in pots next to the seeds; the water which they would first receive was there also in jars, to be specially blessed. The group was busy in prayer. Their bodies swayed back and forth in rhythm with their litany.

This scene took place in this century, in the mid-1950s.

It did not take place in Africa or Borneo. The people praying over their seeds were not Peruvian Indians high in the
Andes. They were Christian Americans and they were in
Los Angeles praying to Jesus Christ that their corn seeds
would grow.

And they did.

In 1959 the Reverend Franklin Loehr wrote a controversial book entitled *The Power of Prayer on Plants*. The
book told of his efforts to determine if praying had any
effect on the rate of growth and germination of seeds. His
procedure was simple enough. Groups of seeds, usually
corn or wheat, were planted in identical containers. The
earth used in the containers was identical. At the last minute, one or the other of the containers was designated as
the "prayer" sample, the other was the control. He and his
group would then pray intently that the chosen seeds would
grow, and most of the seeds in the chosen container grew
faster and taller than their unprayed-for counterparts.
While there were some failures, a statistically significant
sample showed that the prayer seeds germinated and grew
faster than the normal samples, according to the book.

Occasionally the group would not only pray "for" one
group of seeds, but "against" the control sample. Reverend
Loehr reported that these experiments were even more
spectacular. The negated side would often sprout, then
simply shrivel up and die.

Here is a description of a typical experiment:

> . . . (one experimenter) cut six slips of ivy of equal length
> and leafage from his own backyard fence. With a small
> trowel he dug a bit of dirt, mixed it, and filled two small
> pots. He put three ivy slips in each pot, then took them to
> his wife. She chose one to get prayer for growth, which . . .
> (was) then marked with a plus sign. He marked the other

with the minus sign to indicate prayer for non-growth. Then he started prayer work on both. They received the same treatment in every way—water, sunshine, placement, warmth, etc.,—except for the difference in the prayer given them.

All the ivy took root and started to grow, and even at the end of the first week there was not much difference. The growth-prayer plants were thriving, but the non-growth prayer plants were beginning to droop. [He] kept up the prayer treatment for five weeks, at the end of which time the non-growth prayer plants were quite dead.

Another experiment was equally startling. Wet soil was placed in a pan which was divided into two equal halves by a thin piece of wood. Twenty-three corn seeds were placed on each side of the divider. The seeds, and the sides on which they were placed, were chosen at random. Similarly, the side chosen for positive prayer was determined by spinning the pan. Wax paper, spaced off from the soil, covered the whole pan to insure that both groups of seeds were really in the same environment. The prayer continued for eight days. Then:

. . . To say we were astonished at the results when the paper was taken off, is to put it mildly. Sixteen sturdy seedlings greeted us on the positive side. On the negative side there was but one!

But that wasn't all. That one lone seedling, already the smallest of them all, was told he was a brave little fellow, but that he had made a mistake. He wasn't supposed to grow at all. And since he had, he would now be stopped from further growing. Several brief "bursts" of negation-strong mental commands to grow no more were directed at that one seedling, and it *grew no more*. The top of it darkened and withered and it remained in the stunted non-growing condition.

Reverend Loehr later asked a statistician to check the odds of this occurrence being solely due to chance. His answer: two million to one. While this work was not connected directly with any university, Reverend Loehr followed with interest the attempts by some institutions to duplicate his work. He wrote me that the work was "repeatedly duplicated" and "verified" at McGill University and other places.

But what forces were acting? How can human suggestion or supernatural intervention make a plant sprout faster? After a seed has formed on a parent plant, it enters a period of dormancy and is stimulated back into life in the mysterious process of germination. The seeds of some plants such as the Indian Lotus can germinate after lying dormant for hundreds of years; other types of seeds must germinate within a few days after leaving the parent plant or die. Each seed contains an embryo in which the primitive root and plant stem can be identified. In order to germinate, the seed must be warmed to the proper temperature and have adequate oxygen and water. Germination begins when water is absorbed into the seeds. Some seeds will germinate faster if they receive light before being planted. Moisture spreads into the embryo which until that time has been completely dry. This causes the seed to swell and often the hard outside coating cracks under this pressure. When the seed also absorbs oxygen, energy is released and the food stored in the body of the seed itself is conveyed to the centers of growth. Thus stimulated, the root part of the embryo emerges from the seed shell. It develops small root hairs which permit the more rapid absorption of water—and the life of the plant has started.

Even though its exact enzymatic chemistry and genetic interactions are not yet completely understood, the physical process of germination can be thus described. The work of Reverend Loehr suggests that "mind" somehow influenced this physical process. Perhaps the temperature of the favored seeds was improved. Perhaps their supply of water or oxygen was enhanced by suggestion.

Since the 1930s parapsychologists have been seriously experimenting with mind over matter, the phenomenon of psychokinesis, or PK. A significantly large series of experiments conducted over a long period of time with many different experimenters, subjects and strictly controlled techniques have shown that the mind seems to be able to influence the outcome of physical events which should be subject only to the laws of chance.

In a typical PK experiment, dice, as nearly perfect as possible, are rotated in a cage driven by an electric motor. The subject tries to "will" a certain preferred number. The experimenter controls the motor and records the results. After large numbers of runs have been made, the answers usually show that the "willed" number comes up significantly more often than the laws of chance would predict. The advantage to the desired number is so large in a statistical sense, that it seems apparent that some factor other than chance must be at work.

Perhaps this factor was at work for Reverend Loehr also. Perhaps it moved moisture near to the preferred seeds, perhaps it warmed the earth. There have been several recorded cases of abnormal temperature fluctuations associated with extrasensory phenomena. For example, in a well-documented experiment, a temperature drop of 11 degrees Fahrenheit was recorded during a séance of the famous English medium, Stella C. The chill of the séance, in this case at least, was real and registered immutably on an automatic recorder.

The case for Reverend Loehr may rest with PK, a force not yet measured or understood.

The scientific method demands that a given experiment produce results which are repeatable by any experimenter, given the same conditions and circumstances. If the results of the experiment cannot be repeated, then something is lacking; the conclusions drawn from the original experiment are not valid. Yet these plant experiments suggest that the experimenter himself may exert a force, immeasurable by any of our laboratory techniques, which controls the success of the experiment. Furthermore, the experiment may not be repeatable by another scientist simply because he cannot bring the same forces into play. The scientist may say, "I will believe it if I can measure it." If Reverend Loehr is right, something which is immeasurable today may have made the plants grow.

Reverend Loehr has a scientific background. He took his undergraduate degree in chemistry at Monmouth College, Illinois, and through this analytic training developed a respect for experimentation and knowledge of testing techniques. He has been meticulous in his attempts to control the experiments and insure that the only variable was the presence or absence of prayer.

After receiving his degree, Reverend Loehr worked briefly in chemical research at the Dow Chemical Company. He then attended the McCormick Seminary (Presbyterian) in Chicago. During World War II he was a chaplain of an Army Air Force heavy bomber group. After the war he received a series of ministerial assignments which took him finally to the First Congregational Church in Los Angeles in 1950. There he organized a weekly prayer group. In 1952 he, went into religious research full time, and most of his special prayer group participated in the initial plant work. Currently, Reverend Loehr is the research director of the Religious Research Foundation of America, Inc., 663 Fifth Avenue, New York.

Reverend Loehr did not appeal to science to accept his idea. Instead he went directly to the public. He wrote me: "My approach is primarily to the masses—when they accept, the 'leaders' will come around." Clearly this was not the approach taken by most of the other innovators discussed in this book. Before an idea is accepted by natural scientists it must be and generally is, presented to them on their own terms, and judged according to the insight it apparently provides into the workings of nature. It must surpass in predictive precision the theory which it replaces. It must clearly fill a void; there must be a need for the new idea. Perhaps Reverend Loehr sensed that this idea would have to survive a confrontation with the scientific jury to gain any measure of scientific respectability. In August 1965 his Religious Research Foundation co-sponsored a week-long symposium at Princeton, New Jersey. The meeting was devoted to "Developing Unity of Science and Religion." The stated purpose of the session was to "let scientists go beyond the confines of matter," and to "let religionists go beyond the confines of dogma." According to Reverend Loehr, this was to be a "step toward impressing the professorial level, meeting them on the grounds they're occupying."

Our housekeeper was born in the Mexican state of Jalisco in the hills behind Guadalajara. For more years than anyone can remember, she says, the priest has blessed the seeds of the farmers each year in the local church. On a Sunday in late May or early June, before the rains, the pious farmers bring in samples of their seeds, maize, beans, and squash, wrapped in bandannas or in paper bags. After the service, they file by the priest who blesses their seeds with holy water and a Latin phrase. Invariably, she says, crops from the seeds which are blessed outperform those not blessed.

I asked her, if this were so, why all farmers didn't bring their seeds to church that day.

She said that some farmers did not go to church because they didn't have time and others simply forgot, but those who did not come were sorry. How similar this is to the blessing of the shrimp boats in the bayous of Louisiana, or the blessing of the fishing fleets in dozens of coastal cities.

Sometimes a plague of worms or disease attacks the crops in the Mexican hills. Once, in 1950, when my housekeeper and her husband tended their small farm, and tilled the soil with a crude plow and a mule, worms infested their crop. They were little gray, hard, ugly worms, with green bellies and they gnawed at the roots of the corn plants. The crop started to die. The government advised that certain insecticides be used. These proved ineffective. Then, as Mexican farmers have done for hundreds, perhaps thousands of years, they hired the priest. For twenty-five centavos he came to their farm. With a little bowl of holy water he walked between the stalks of corn in his fine robes, sprinkling the water first to the right and then to the left, reading from his Bible. He walked along the furrows the full day and, by the time he left, the worms were dead—dead by the thousands.

To this my housekeeper will swear, and so will her people. To them it is not unusual. Perhaps the insecticide finally worked, or perhaps her hypothesis and that of Reverend Loehr's is true. This Indian woman is saying what men have believed for more years than history can record

—magic, or at least belief, can affect and control nature.

Since the earliest glimmering of prehistory the advent of spring, the sudden bursting forth of green, verdurous, living things, in place of the barren winter, has been a source of wonder, a piece of supreme magic to watching man. When trees were bare and the sky cold with the sun low on the horizon, early man must have wondered, "Will the warmth return?" He could never be sure. His experience was limited by the racial memory of his immediate group. Almost naturally, perhaps instinctively as psychologist Carl Jung suggests, the primitive man turned to magic to bring back the spring, to make things grow. And this magic was rewarded by the slow climbing of the sun back toward the zenith and the growth of living things. Only a brave man or a fool would have watched the shortening days of winter without hoping that the magical entreaties for the return of spring would once again be successful.

At a certain stage in the development of a primitive society man seems to have believed that the means for ending winter, making rain fall, the sun shine, the spring begin; in short, controlling or directing nature, was in his hands. Accordingly, he practiced magic rites to control nature. As Sir James Frazer points out, when man became more sophisticated and knowledgeable he attributed the steady alterations of day and night, of winter and summer, and of life and death to the struggles of their gods who, loving, living, fighting, and dying in a colossal but human pattern, caused the changing environment presented to man. Then primitive magic changed to superstition, and the rites were directed to the support of the battles of the gods, particularly the god-figure that represented life. Early civilizations believed that winter came when this god-life force fell ill or was dying or banished from heaven in his eternal struggle with the god-death force. Through magic-religious rites, man helped his hero ascend again, and winter turned to spring.

Through all of this ran the theme: Man can affect nature by hoping enough. Man can make seeds germinate.

The invention of prayer as a means of communication with God has its roots deep in Jewish history. Prayer is one of the two great contributions of the Jews. In the age of the Prophets three thousand years ago, when Judaism was being solidified into an ethic, the Jews created two new ideas: first, a place of worship was not necessarily a place of sacrifice and it could be set up anywhere; and second, communication with God could take place through prayer. This concept of the holy place being a house of prayer followed into the Christian churches and the Moslem mosques, and a metaphysics relating to the proper way to pray, the validity of prayer, the relationship of prayer to the individual and his deity, arose. It was an extension of the old mysticism: a prayer had to have the correct formulation, the right intonations, the proper timing. God had to be addressed by the proper name and with or without a covering on the head. But basically prayer was and is an expression of the individual. A plea for help made to forces which he cannot comprehend, a litany of self-confession, a hint of psychoanalysis, a call from the subconscious to the supernatural.

Prayer is almost universal; yet when one suggests that prayer can, in fact, produce the physical results prayed for, the skeptics raise a holy howl. The scientists say: Where is the force? The theologians say: The will of God cannot be measured. The press says: Bunk.

Robert Hatch, well-known literary critic, reported in the *Nation:*

> . . . The fact is that Dr. Loehr, for all his scientific cackle and unctuous sermonizing, is an old-fashioned magician. He does not petition God for aid, he commands nature to forsake its ways and follow him . . . All this, I make bold to say is nonsense . . .

Another newspaper said simply:

> The editors of Doubleday must have been out to lunch when this book was accepted.

Reverend Loehr told me about a newspaper critic who was attempting to compose a column about the book. The newspaper had received a prepublication copy some weeks before it appeared in the bookstores and various staff members had performed the basic experiment right in the city room—with positive results. But this was an afternoon paper and the morning paper had given the book a favorable review, so a different slant was obviously needed. Reverend Loehr says:

> . . . So [the newspaperman] called those professors (from UCLA, USC and Occidental College) who all said in essence it *could* not be done—and three prominent clergymen (different faiths) who all said in essence it *should* not be done. Then he reported this to me and asked for a comment. I simply said, "Sorry, we did it!"

Where does it all lead? If it can be shown that prayer can lead to physical, measurable effects, what does this mean to man? First, to the scientist it will portend a new kind of uncertainty principle which states that the wishes of the experimenter may affect the results of his experiment. This effect would be manifested not in a subconscious manipulation of the data or experimental procedure, but through a real external force. Dr. Rhine's PK experiments suggest that this can happen. Perhaps this is why some experimenters seem to be able to "make things fall into place."

Dr. John C. Lilly, a scientist deeply committed to serious experimental research in the field of neurophysiology, puts it this way:

> Many times a rather eerie experience occurs. When the chief investigator leaves the room, something happens that makes the whole experiment disintegrate. In long twenty-four hour runs I have often left the preparation in the hands of an assistant and gone home to get some sleep, only to be awakened from my sleep by the assistant saying that something has gone wrong in my absence. Going back to the laboratory I either find that it is an easily correctable defect in the apparatus, or that the alleged defect disappears while I am present. At times this coincidence is so remarkable that I feel there is no logical reason for it and that the "in-tune" process has roots far deeper than we can understand at the present time. However, such experiences occur only when I am deeply involved with the apparatus and with the [experimental] animal in question over a sufficiently long period of time so that, as it were, there is a miniature replica of the experiment continuously going on in my own head. This situation occurs only with unremitting, uninterrupted effort over many days and weeks; such preparation may be part of the "in-tune" phenomena.

This one-ness with an experiment or an apparatus or piece of equipment, which Dr. Lilly calls the "in-tune" phenomena, is not a strange concept to my wife. My work requires that I travel quite frequently. Almost invariably, when I return from a trip, my wife, who is notoriously nonmechanical (is "artistic" better?), will report that some of our many appliances have ceased to function. Of course I simply plug them in or flip the proper switch and, for some reason, incredibly, the machines begin to function again. "I knew it," she'll say with some disbelief, "those *things* know when you're back in town."

Theologians would also discover an anathema. With measurements of the force of prayer, and demonstration that prayer is a means by which an individual may exert a degree of control over his environment, the mysticism, the supernatural aspects of prayer might be removed. God would still exist, but He would not be the agent or the means of execution of the supplications of the faithful. A God-force would become a man-force.

What this confirmation would mean to the people, I can only guess. A means of affecting crop yield? A means of weather control?

There is the question: Is prayer a remnant of mysticism or does the religious folklore that surrounds prayer have some basis in demonstrable fact? Can we not devise a critical test? If Loehr's work is valid, will someone else try?

# (8

# THE
# THIRD
# LEVEL

Professor William Wolf, presently of the School of Business Administration, University of Southern California, told me about the time he was lecturing at the University of Washington, in Seattle. His son was in the hospital with bronchial pneumonia. In the middle of the lecture, Professor Wolf had a strong feeling that he "had to go to the hospital." He cut his lecture short and rushed to his son's room. He found him unattended; the air hose to his oxygen tent had broken.

Another time he had a strangely realistic dream that someone was calling him. The dream woke him at four A.M. and it had been so disturbing that he lay awake until dawn trying to determine if some noise in the house could have stimulated the dream. For reasons he didn't understand Professor Wolf got up and placed a long distance call to his parents. He found out that his mother had been in an automobile accident and had been pinned under a car for three hours without help. The accident had occurred at about the time of his dream.

I asked the professor what it felt like to "receive." There is no discrete sensation, apparently. He said, "You really aren't certain that you are receiving anything. In fact, it is only a vague feeling that one should do something or that something has happened. It is barely on the conscious level except as a general feeling of anxiety." He isn't consciously aware of what has happened or even why he is acting; yet knows that in time of stress, people close to him have been able to alert him to their desire to communicate.

A definition of terms is probably in order at this point. Extrasensory perception (ESP) is perception by an individual through means other than sight, taste, hearing, smell, or touch. It includes *clairvoyance,* which is the understanding or sensing of events at a remote distance by a single person; *precognition,* which is the sensing of events that will occur at some time in the future; *psychokinesis,* which is the ability to influence matter through thought; and *telepathy,* which is the sending of thoughts by one person and the receiving and understanding of these thoughts by another.

Clairvoyance seems to function most effectively in times of stress or imminent danger. It seems to cover distance without any loss in efficiency, which of course makes the phenomenon dangerously opposed to materialistic physical science. I speak as though clairvoyance is an established fact. It is not, of course, an "accredited" phenomenon, simply because its mechanism cannot be explained, even in the most primitive way. Yet the fact that individual perception across space can occur has been demonstrated in the laboratory many times. It is these laboratory tests that lend credence to the personal stories of perception across space that have been recorded in the nonscientific literature, unexplained, for three thousand years.

Here is the way tests were run at Duke University. The subject was seated at a table and shown a deck of cards. The deck was a special one, composed of twenty-five cards made up of five different symbols. The deck was shuffled, placed face down on the table, and the subject was asked to identify the top card without either the experimenter or the subject having looked at it. After he called out his guess, the card was removed by the experimenter. The guess was recorded but the card was not inspected at this time. Then the subject gave his guess on the next card, and so on through the deck until all cards had been called. Then the experimenter recorded the order of the cards and checked them against the calls. The subject was told immediately of his results in most tests and encouraged. Then the cards were shuffled by the experimenter and the procedure was repeated.

In this type of experiment, the odds are fairly easy to compute. The subject could be expected to hit five cards out of twenty-five, just by chance. Now in scientific experimentation, if consistent results can be produced that are different than those expected by pure chance, it can be concluded that some force is at work other than chance. Ordinarily, the results are called significant if the phenomenon being demonstrated beats the laws of chance by a factor of 100 or so. The Duke experiments in clairvoyance often produced results with over one million to one odds that something other than pure chance was at work.

In the first three years of his work in the early 1930s, Dr. J. B. Rhine, the venerable ESP researcher of Duke, found a subject who went through the deck over 700 times and averaged eight hits per run. Of these results, Dr. Rhine says:

> . . . To express the odds against averaging a score of 8 or
> better by chance alone for more than 700 runs would require
> a paragraph of figures. This performance of one individual is
> so significant, and rules out chance so completely, that it
> does not matter what any of the other subjects did. No
> matter what their scores, they could not nullify the striking
> extrachance character of this one man's performance!

But all the results were published. In this series of experiments the subjects had been selected in a pre-screening run
through a deck. Those subjects who called over six cards
correctly were invited to participate in the body of the experiment. Nevertheless, all data, even those from the rejected applicants, were included in the final report. Over
85,000 single card calls were made and the over-all average
was better than seven hits per deck of twenty-five cards.
During the experiment one subject incredibly called all
twenty-five cards correctly.

I reported on this test series in such detail because it
marked the real beginning of laboratory controlled contemporary testing of parapsychological phenomena. Many,
but not all, experimenters have been able to achieve or ex-
ceed these results since Dr. Rhine's early experiments.
Hence one of the tenets of the scientific method is *almost*
satisfied: the ability to replicate a set of data by anyone at
any time. But "almost" is a big word in science; it is enough
to exclude ESP from orthodoxy. Furthermore, and perhaps
more seriously, every hypothesis proposed to explain the
phenomenon has proved to be inadequate.

In an effort to construct hypotheses, various experimenters
such as Dr. Gardner Murphy of the Menninger Foundation
in Topeka, Kansas, have been interested in checking the
effect of distance between the experimenter and his subject
on the accuracy of the results. Studies involving separation

distances from a few feet to thousands of miles have all indicated the presence of ESP to levels well beyond pure chance. So far no correlation between the separation distance and the accuracy of the data has been found. Other experimenters, such as Thelma Moss of UCLA have tried shielding their subjects to remove all sensory cues and to isolate their environment. Still others such as Dr. Gertrude Schmeider of City College of New York are working to attempt to correlate ESP performance with the subject's personality traits and other psychological factors.

Yet there exists no working hypothesis for clairvoyance; in fact, there is no hypothesis that I know of that can even begin to explain ESP in general, in terms acceptable to the body of physical science tests. So today we have a large body of popular unscientific anecdotes attesting to clairvoyance in individual experience, and extensive laboratory experimentation that confirms the effect, but no explanation.

There are many accounts of personal clairvoyance. Some people have apparently developed this talent to a precise and practical degree. One such man was Edgar Cayce, a fairly well-known and controversial figure until his death in 1947. Ostensibly clairvoyant, he could call up images at a distance at will.

Two biographies have been written about this man. He was either an insidious and dangerous fraud or he had somehow tapped a source of knowledge closed to most men. Cayce was billed as a medical clairvoyant. Upon request, he ostensibly could "see" people who were ill, "see" down into their bodies, find the site of their maladies and tell them the causes of their problems and the cures. For most of his career he gave readings from his home in Virginia Beach, Virginia. The person he was diagnosing did not have to be present. Rather he would write Cayce, telling where he would be on a particular day and at a particular time. Then, at the proper time, Edgar Cayce would relax, fall into a semi-hypnotic state, and visualize the person and his medical or psychological problems. He would describe his symptoms and often the cause and potential cure. The fact that a man might attempt such a presumptive artifice is not in itself surprising; the fact that he was often apparently right, is.

A reading would begin with Cayce's wife or his son or a close associate giving him the suggestion that he find a particular individual at a particular street address in a certain town and state. Cayce was asked in this initial suggestion to examine the subject's body carefully and thoroughly, tell the conditions he found there, and suggest means of relieving or helping "the body." Cayce often would begin to speak about a detail of the subject's town or neighborhood, the room he was in, the weather, or the scenery. According to Dr. Cerminara, a Ph.D. from the University of Wisconsin, who investigated Cayce, these initial descriptions "invari ably proved accurate."

Cayce would then proceed into his diagnosis and prescription. All of his statements were transcribed and kept on record at Virginia Beach, and still exist. Dr. Cerminara searched these files in her study of Cayce and cites the following case as an example of his work:

> . . . a young girl in Selma, Alabama . . . unaccountably lost her reason and was committed to a mental institution. Her brother, deeply concerned, requested Cayce's help. Cayce lay down on his couch, took a few deep breaths, and put himself to sleep. He then accepted a brief hypnotic suggestion that he see and diagnose the body of the girl in question. After a pause of a few moments he began to speak, as all hypnotic subjects will when so instructed. Unlike most hypnotic subjects, however, he began to outline . . . the physical condition of the demented girl. He stated that one

of her wisdom teeth was impacted, and was thus impinging on a nerve in the brain. Removal of the tooth, he said, would relieve the pressure and restore the girl to normalcy. Examination was made of the area of the mouth which he described; the unsuspected impaction was found. Appropriate dental surgery resulted in a complete return to sanity.

It all began this way: In 1900, when Cayce was twenty-three, he discovered his talent through a very strange set of circumstances. He had had a debilitating loss of his voice that lasted for over a year. No medication seemed to help him and he and his doctors finally came to believe his disease was incurable. One evening at the Opera House in Hopkinsville, Kentucky, he met a traveling hypnotist, a Mr. Hart, "the Laugh King," who offered to try to help him while under hypnosis. Sure enough, his voice returned while he was hypnotized, but posthypnotic suggestion did not seem to work. After Mr. Hart left, another hypnotist tried but also **failed. Finally, almost in desperation,** Cayce asked a third **hypnotist, a Mr. Al Layne, to try his hand. This time**, acting on a suggestion made by a northern doctor, Layne asked Cayce to describe his ailment while he was in a trance. To Layne's surprise Cayce did just that. He said that the laryngitis was caused by a partial paralysis of the inferior muscles of the vocal cords and that increasing the circulation to these muscles would improve the condition. Layne suggested that Cayce increase his circulation to these areas and soon Cayce's throat and upper chest turned red. After twenty minutes or so, Cayce said, "It's all right now. The condition is removed. Make the suggestion that the circulation return to normal." Layne did this and awakened Cayce, who could then speak for the first time in a year. There were some relapses, but each time this hypnotic treatment was repeated until finally he was cured.

Layne and Cayce continued the experiments, but now directing Cayce's hypnotic self to look into other bodies than his own during the trances. Layne was the first such subject. Soon there were others. His file gradually grew as his fame spread and his apparent cures became known.

The fact that there were apparent cures, that he did seem to know details of the people he was treating and their physical environment although he was thousands of miles away, that he used medical language with which he was consciously unfamiliar, seems almost certain.

It was probably inevitable that the paths of Edgar Cayce and Dr. Rhine should cross. Jess Stearn, who conducted considerable research into Cayce's clairvoyance, reported that in 1935 Dr. Rhine attempted to set up a test with Cayce. He was to identify the contents of a package in a filing case locked in a room at Columbia University. At first the experiment didn't interest Cayce, but his son Hugh Lynn urged him to try because of the recognition it would bring. Cayce agreed, but the board of the Association for Research and Enlightenment, which at the time essentially directed Cayce's activities, turned him down. While it is not evidence we can class as a laboratory experiment, Cayce's son remembers his father once named all fifty-two cards in a face-down deck.

Cayce and Dr. Rhine met again once in 1936, when the doctor asked for a reading on his three-year-old daughter, Betsy. The reading was given, but was rejected strenuously when it didn't agree with the medical diagnosis Dr. Rhine had been given. Stearn goes on to say:

> . . . By speech and written word, Rhine has since blasted Cayce and the Cayce movement. In 1955, speaking before a Dallas group, he made a slighting reference to Cayce's reading of his daughter; witnesses reported him saying the treat-

ment called for "a machine or battery which he learned much later was sold by a front for Cayce or the Association."

Stearn says that Cayce would not have profited from the sale of a machine, it was an electrical wet cell incidentally, and in any event, it was offered free to Dr. Rhine. While the ailment was not disclosed in the literature available to me, the use of such a therapeutic device is difficult to understand.

It is indeed unfortunate that these two men did not reach some rapport. How valuable it would have been if Cayce's clairvoyance could have been examined in a laboratory.

A friend of mine, whom I will call Mr. R, told me this remarkable story. For weeks he had been looking forward to a hunting trip with several of his close friends. They were to go duck hunting in the marsh country at the opening of the season. They had been out together several times before and this trip promised to be one of the best, since each had arranged for several days off. My friend, Mr. R purchased shells for the trip, cleaned off his shotgun and prepared his decoys. They laid out the material they would need for the duck blind and arranged for a cabin near the marsh in which they would hunt. I mention this detail of the preparations for the trip to show that it was not a spur-of-the-moment thing; each member of the party was looking forward to it, particularly Mr. R who made this trip to hunt ducks every year.

Their enthusiasm was high. The night before the trip to the marsh, Mr. R set his alarm clock for four-thirty. His friends were to pick him up at five. He went to bed full of anticipation. Everything was ready for the trip.

The next morning his alarm clock went off, and Mr. R arose, shaved and dressed in his warm flannels. He took down his shotgun, got his shells and other equipment, and after a quick cup of coffee, went out to his front porch to wait for his friends.

They drove up about five minutes late and waved him down to the car.

"Come on," they said. "Let's get going."

He started down. There were about twenty steps from the porch to the sidewalk. He took the first few rapidly, his rifle over his shoulder. Then he started to walk slower and slower. Finally he stopped, halfway down.

He was cold. He was shivering in fact. Something was wrong. He knew, somehow, he should not go on this trip. It wasn't a vague uneasiness; it was a certainty. He must not go.

"I'm not going," he said slowly, hardly realizing that he had said it, and certainly not understanding why.

"Not going? But you're all dressed. You've got your gun, your shells. What do you mean you're not going?"

"Just what I said. I'm not going." Mr. R could not explain it to them or himself. He simply knew he should not go on this particular trip at this particular time. He knew it when he started down the steps. He knew it when he turned cold.

"And," he continued, "if I were you I wouldn't go either. I just don't feel right about it. Why don't you guys come in and have some breakfast?"

"Are you crazy?" they asked. "We're going on. See you later."

They drove off leaving Mr. R standing on the steps, wondering about himself. He turned to climb back up the steps, shotgun still on his shoulder.

He went back into the house and sat quietly in the living room waiting to have breakfast with his wife. He wondered what he would tell her that would not sound foolish.

Before she was up, the wife of one of his friends called.

She was sobbing and was shocked to hear him answer the phone.

"Didn't you go?" she asked incredulously. "They had an awful accident. The police just called. The car went over a cliff and they were all killed. We thought you were with them."

Mr. R hung up the phone and waited for breakfast with his wife.

Mr. R is a bright, serious engineer working on our space program, not normally given to histrionics. Yet he believes that he somehow has the ability to sense danger lying in his future.

When he was a teenager he owned a motorcycle and belonged to what would today be called a leather-jacket rat pack. The group generally raised hell, speeding down the back country roads when they thought they could get away with it. There were a few scrapes with the police, but even more seriously, one or the other of the group would occasionally lose control of his bike. The recklessness gradually began to catch up with them. First one, then another of their group was killed.

The boys weren't impressed. That was the other guy's problem. A boy under twenty can feel a sense of invincibility, of death being for the other guy, not for him, particularly on a motorcycle, with the throbbing, roaring engine under him, wind in his face and the open road ahead.

One day Mr. R was riding down the coast highway at a reasonable speed, not worried, not thinking about anything in particular except the control of his machine and the surf and the sun. He felt good.

For the first time in his life he perceived he was in trouble. It was a sudden realization, a flash of intuition. When he told me this story, he put it this way: *he got the message.*

Somehow he knew that he would be next. He would crash and die on his motorcycle. The thought was so sudden and incongruous with his feeling of a few seconds before that he was thoroughly shaken. He pulled to the side of the road and got off the bike. He really had "the message."

He started his motorcycle again and inched his way home. To the relief of his family he announced that he was going to give up the sport, and he placed a for sale advertisement in the local newspaper.

Because he was so eager to be rid of the bike he set a low price on it and sold it quickly. The new owner came and looked it over. Mr. R couldn't have known what was going to happen.

The new owner kicked the starter and drove off with a roar. About half an hour later the motorcycle was wrecked and he was dead.

This is precognition—realization of what's going to happen in the future; more than realization, a certainty, conviction. It is prophecy, that strangest of phenomena that primitive man has always believed without question and sophisticated man has never believed, even with a semblance of proof available.

The whole edifice of science is built on the ability to prophesy. Natural laws are, after all, formulas for predicting. Some scientific disciplines permit relatively exact predictions; others predict with less precision. Those that are exact are rigid sciences; those that are approximate have been called semi-sciences. Psychology, jurisprudence, molecular biology, and group dynamics are examples of disciplines in which causality is not completely understood. In these types of fields, expert opinion is admissible. It is the expert who can predict; he is recognized as an expert because of the accuracy of his previous predictions.

In the semi-sciences the expert may work from his integrated unverbalized experience and observations which somehow in his mind become the equivalent of causality. The expert who can predict accurately will achieve stature in his discipline.

Therefore, in science, prediction occurs on two levels; that based on observed cause and effect and that based on inferred causality and intuition. Yet, there is apparently a third level of prediction which does not answer to causality and does not require an expert. This is precognition, which is the antithesis of science. In precognition, some people, distinguished by a trait which cannot yet be identified, seem able to predict without previous observation, without cause and effect. To be able to predict an event in the future which is unrelated to an event in the present is not only unscientific, it is anti-scientific, since it somehow puts the effect before the cause, the perceiving before the occurrence. To theologians it smacks of absolute predestination and the nonexistence of free determinism, which must concern the Church, all biblical prophets notwithstanding.

Dr. Rhine believes that prophecy is the "strangest of all human powers." Even though his experiments indicate the existence of precognition or something that behaves like it, he has said:

> . . . It is hard to understand how the act of perception, which is the result, could occur before its cause. From the viewpoint of present knowledge, it is inconceivable that the precognition could really occur. If there were ever an occasion in science on which it would be proper to use the word impossible, it would be when the hypothesis of prophecy was advanced.

Yet it happens. The literature is rich with first person experiences. Volumes have been collected about the flash of danger sensed before a trip, about the sudden realization that a loved one would die.

Before President Abraham Lincoln was assassinated, he dreamed a most peculiar, a most frightening dream. He talked about his dream one evening in the second week of April 1865 to his old friend Ward Lamon, to Mrs. Lincoln and to one or two other friends. They were in the White House and their conversation had turned to dreams and their meanings. This discussion was so unusual that Lamon made notes immediately afterward of Lincoln's own words and these have been recorded. Historians have studied these notes and have reported his bizarre episode:

Lincoln talked for a while, slowly, about dreams and how the Bible was filled with prophecy. He was tired and was drawn with melancholy. He said:

> . . . About ten days ago I retired very late. I had been up waiting for important dispatches from the front. I could not have been long in bed when I fell into a slumber, for I was weary. I soon began to dream. There seemed to be a death-like stillness about me. Then I heard subdued sobs, as if a number of people were weeping. I thought I left my bed and wandered downstairs. There the silence was broken by some pitiful sobbing, but the mourners were invisible. I went from room to room; no living person was in sight, but the same mournful sounds of distress met me as I passed along. It was light in all the rooms; every object was familiar to me; but where were all the people who were grieving as if their hearts would break? I was puzzled and alarmed. What could be the meaning of all this. Determined to find the cause of a state of things so mysterious and so shock-ing, I kept on until I arrived at the East Room, which I entered. There I met with a sickening surprise. Before me was a catafalque, on which rested a corpse wrapped in funeral vestments. Around it were stationed soldiers who were acting as guards; and there was a throng of people,

some gazing mournfully upon the corpse, whose face was covered, others weeping pitifully.

"Who is dead in the White House?" I demanded of one of the soldiers.

"The President," was his answer; "he was killed by an assassin!"

Then came a large burst of grief from the crowd, which awoke me from my dream. I slept no more that night; and although it was only a dream, I have been strangely annoyed by it ever since.

President Lincoln died April 15, 1865. His body was laid in a coffin in the East Room of the White House. It was guarded by soldiers as long lines of weeping mourners passed by. The scene must have been almost exactly as Lincoln described it.

One of the most famous stories about precognition surrounds the murder of Julius Caesar. Plutarch wrote that Caesar's wife Calpurnia dreamed the night before his assassination in the Senate. Caesar and his wife were together in bed, asleep. Suddenly the wind blew open the doors and windows. This startled Caesar and he sat bolt upright in the bed. In the moonlight he could see Calpurnia, still asleep, but obviously dreaming. She was groaning and muttering some indistinct words. When she woke she told him that she had been weeping over Caesar, holding his butchered body in her arms.

Another story of her dream is that she saw the pinnacle which the Senate had ordered erected over Caesar's house as a mark of his office and grandeur, tumbling down and crushed into the dust.

She begged Caesar not to go out that day, to call off the meeting of the Senate, or at very least if he didn't believe her, to consult the oracles. Now Plutarch says that Caesar was very impressed by Calpurnia's importuning because she wasn't usually superstitious. He consulted his priests and they also found the oracles "inauspicious." At that point Caesar resolved to call off the session that day, but his confidant, Decimus Albinus, who was in on the plot against his life, persuaded him that he should go through with the meeting, for this was the day he was to be declared king of all the provinces, and his enemies would make much of the fact that he had let the dream of a woman keep him from such an important meeting.

So Caesar went on to the Senate and kept his appointment on the Ides of March.

No discussion about prophecy would be complete without at least a brief look at one of the most imposing characters in this foggy, mystic never-never land, Nostradamus.

Nostradamus was the assumed name of Michel de Notre-dame, a French Jew, a physician and astrologer who lived from 1503 to 1566. He studied medicine at the great universities of Avignon and Montpellier. He was a good physician for the time apparently, because when the black plague broke out in the South of France, he achieved great distinction for his cures. But he is most famous today for his prophecies. These were published in 1555, as a book titled *Centuries*. The *Centuries* was composed of groups of quatrains, grouped into hundreds, each one hundred verses labeled a century. The book is still being read by Nostradamus scholars to see if, somehow, this man caught a glimpse of the future.

Many of his critics claim that the verses are much too obscure, that anything at all can be read into them. In scanning the verses, one gets the feeling that somehow these stanzas *are* history, or history to be, and when a verse seems obscure

it is only so because the reader can't quite recall the events
which Nostradamus is describing.

The Nostradamus scholars say the meanings of the verses
are clear enough if only they are studied. They believe that
the old master wrote in anagrams, substituting, for example,
Hister for Hitler, or Pau Nay Loron for Napoleon. This of
course opens his predictions to a great deal of interpretation,
but these scholars say that the words are clear enough for
anyone who wants to take the trouble to look. Some of their
interpretative translations seem to be stretching to make history fit the verses; others seem to show a spark of knowledge
of the future. Here's one such verse:

> . . . *The husband alone afflicted will be mitred on his re-*
> *turn.*
> A *conflict will take place at the Tuileries by five hundred*
> *men.*
> *One traitor will be titled—Narbon;*
> *And (the other) Saulce, grandfather oilman, will (hand*
> *him) over to the soldiery.*

The reference to the Tuileries clearly places the scene in
Paris. When this quatrain was written, however, the Tuileries didn't exist as a royal palace, but was, as the name
implies, a tile kiln. Could the verse be a forgery then?
Apparently not. Some research reported by Stearn shows
that an edition of Nostradamus' work dated 1672 also includes this quatrain. This edition predates the French Revolution by more than a hundred years.

The husband, Louis XVI, was the King of France during
the French Revolution. On June 20, 1791, he and his wife
Marie Antoinette fled from their palace in Paris and attempted, in disguise, to leave the country. They were discovered at a small town of Varennes. The mayor of the town

was away so the procurer exercised his authority and stopped the travelers. His name was Sauce! He, his father, and his grandfather were the grocers of the town and dealt in oil and candles. The King and Queen were held in a room over the grocery while waiting for their armed escort back to the city.

Comte de Narbonne was the King's Minister of War from December 6, 1791 to March 9, 1792. He was dismissed by Louis because of his overambition and "the indiscretions of his mistress." Thus: the titled traitor—Narbon.

On June 20, 1792, a crowd of Parisians attacked the Tuileries and invaded the quarters of the King. There they made him put on a red cap, a mitre, the famous *bonnet rouge*, symbol of militant patriotism of revolutionary France. The husband, afflicted, was thus mitred on his return.

On July 30, 1792, the young French patriot, Charles-Jean-Marie Barbaroux, brought five hundred and sixteen National Guardsmen of Marseille and Toulon into Paris. He had said: "They knew how to die," and these were the men who brought the *Hymne des Marseillaise* with them. They fought, and some of them died, in the final attack on the Tuileries.

If the verse is genuine, as it seems to be, it is truly remarkable.

There's much more, of course, about the revolution such as:

> *The assembly will condemn the King taken,*
> *(And) the Queen taken to death by jurors sworn by lot;*
> *They will deny life to the Dauphin,*
> *And the prostitute at the fort will partake of the same fate.*

This is almost an exact if somewhat incomplete description of the fate of Louis and Marie Antoinette. Their son, the Dauphin, was not executed on the guillotine because of his age, but was taken to prison to die. The courtesan Madame Du Barry was arrested and guillotined in 1793, thus sharing the fate of her consort. Again this quatrain seems to be authentic and, at least in retrospect, fits history. But the quatrains lack a certain amount of practicality which would be necessary for their efficient use: if Du Barry had read Nostradamus before she returned to France she wouldn't have found her name there. Only after she lost her head could we recognize her in the old seer's lines.

Napoleon, his ascendancy to power, his military victories, his defeats, his exile to Elba, even his insignia of a bee can be found with the same type of retrospection. If you try you can find the American Revolution, the Civil War, the World Wars, the problems of the League of Nations, and the rise of Communism.

I found one that seemed appropriate, now that the Gemini space flights are being conducted:

> *. . . Shall a monarch be killed a little before?*
> *Caster and Pollux (the Gemini twins) in the ship, a comet;*
> *The public brass shall be emptied by land and sea,*
> *Pisa, Asti, Ferrara, Turin a land laid under interdict.*

I don't know how the Italian towns got in there, but that sounds like the Gemini program all right. It came after the death of President Kennedy, and it certainly is emptying the public brass.

There are other verses which tell of the Orientals overrunning Western Europe ". . . He shall pass through the sky, the waters and snow, and shall strike everyone with his rod." I hope I'm wrong when I guess at the nature of the Chinese rod.

Nostradamus talks of floods, "a new and sudden, impetuous rain . . . stone from heaven, fires shall make the sea stony." And in another quatrain: ". . . a great fire from heaven shall fall for three nights . . . very soon afterwards the earth shall quake." And in yet another:

> . . . *After a great human exhaustion, a greater is made*
> *ready,*
> *The great motor renews the ages:*
> *A plague of blood, milk, famine, iron and plague,*
> *In the heavens shall be seen fire, a long running spark.*

Is this related to Velikovsky's proposition in some unholy way? Are we to find our end in another Exodus?

Next to Nostradamus ranks my mother-in-law, the prophet. My mother-in-law is a witch. She reads tea leaves. I've often asked her how she does it but the best she can do is to say that the leaves show her small pictures and she simply "knows" what they mean. Here's what she's been able to do with her tea pictures: six months before my first child arrived, she predicted the sex, the date and time of birth, and was accurate to within eight minutes. For my second child she predicted only the sex and was correct. Early in my wife's third pregnancy she read in the tea leaves that we would have twins, one boy and one girl, and that the boy would be born first and breech. The doctor steadfastly maintained that my wife was carrying only a single baby. Finally, a month before the birth date, the doctor confirmed that twins were coming. And in fact they were a boy and a girl, the boy did come first and breech. How far can a daughter cooperate?

Dr. Rhine started working with scientific precognition experiments in 1933. In these early tests the special deck of twenty-five cards with five symbols was placed face down on a table. The subject was asked to try to identify the order in which these cards would appear after they were shuffled.

His prediction was recorded by the experimenter who was separated from the subject by an opaque screen. Then, after all the answers were given, the experimenter shuffled the deck, and cut them. Then they were turned over in sequence and compared to the predictions given. By pure chance, the subjects should have hit five cards out of the deck of twenty-five. But there were significantly more hits than this.

Of these tests, Dr. Rhine said:

> The score averages . . . were comparatively low, between 5 and 6 hits per 25 calls. But the scores were consistent enough through the more than 4,500 runs that the odds were 400,000 to one that chance alone did not produce the total score obtained . . . These results certainly suggested pre-cognition . . .

In still other tests the cards were shuffled by machine, or the subjects were asked to pre-identify which of five choices would be picked by a random selection machine. All these tests produced similar results. Something was apparently at work other than pure chance.

A salesman was out on a long road trip heading to South Bend, Indiana. He was thinking of nothing in particular when suddenly he *knew* that he had to go to Fort Wayne. Now he hadn't intended to go to Fort Wayne and he had no interest in going there, but he headed there anyway. He felt he was a victim of an overactive imagination. As he came closer to the city he realized that his going to Fort Wayne was connected in some way with a tragedy in his family. To discover the tragedy he would have to go to the leading hotel and ask for a message.

When he arrived, there was in fact a message for him. It was from his wife. Their little daughter was dying.

Later, his wife was asked why she sent the telegram to Fort Wayne. She said that she simply thought he would get it there.

And so the stories go. The man who is buried and summons aid by thinking about his co-worker, the co-worker feeling that he simply had to go to that place; or aborigines who ostensibly communicate through telepathy; the knowledge of the panic of a loved one.

This is telepathy: the transference of thought from one person to another. There is a tremendous amount of anecdotal literature here too. Once again the laboratory tests seem to confirm that forces other than chance are at work. Mrs. Thelma Moss of the Department of Psychology at the University of California at Los Angeles has recently completed a series of tests different from the more routine guess-what-card-comes-next type. She reasoned that these stereotyped tests have very little in common with the real life situation in which the receiver of a telepathy "team" is often relaxed and the sender is often highly agitated and excited. She tried to design and conduct an experiment in which a telepathic relationship would be established between an emotion-charged sender and a relaxed receiver. She reported on this startling work, which is as yet unpublished, at a symposium on extrasensory perception held at UCLA on June 5 and 6, 1965.

She placed the transmitter of the pair in a specially designed soundproof isolation booth. The receiver was in a separate room. The transmitter was shown a group of slides pertaining to a highly emotional situation. For example, one slide sequence showed the Nazi gas ovens and dead, decaying bodies stacked on one another. These slides were accompanied by raucous, tearing music played over a set of earphones worn by the transmitter. Another set of slides showed the assassination of President Kennedy. In all, each transmitter was shown six sets of slide situations. As these slides were shown the transmitter spoke into a small microphone, recording the emotion which he himself felt while watching a set of slides. In the other room, the receiver did not know what was going on. He was relaxed, and was stretched out on a cot. A microphone was placed nearby to record any emotion or image he felt was being sent. The comments of the transmitter and the comments of the receiver which were recorded on tape were later transcribed verbatim by a stenographer. These comments were typed on separate cards. Thirty teams were used, and just to make things fair, a group of ten "receivers" were matched to nonexistent transmitters. These people served as the control group. The cards were then all randomized and six judges, all psychologists, were asked to match the cards of a transmitter and receiver team based only on the comments typed on the cards. Of the six judges, two were openly in favor of the experiment and ESP in general, two were opposed and two were neutral.

Here are the results as reported by Mrs. Moss. Pure chance, or random matching of receiver to transmitter responses would have permitted the judges to match two or more cards in a set of six 48% of the time. However, they actually matched 78% of the responses. The odds against this being chance are better than one in a thousand. The control group showed chance or less than chance results.

In discussing the results of the experiment Mrs. Moss said:

> . . . Even more encouraging are the verbatim responses of certain receivers. For example, one transmitter of one team was given a scene showing the ocean, Hawaii, tranquillity; the receiver in the next room said, and I'm quoting this verbatim, "For some strange reason, I seem to be in Hono-

lulu in the Hawaiian Islands. There's an atmosphere of
holiday, relaxation and rest, palm trees and green things
growing and blooming bright colored flowers. Perhaps I'm
sitting in a pool. Everything is restful and peaceful."

And there were other responses equally as startling. As in
other studies, Mrs. Moss found that some receivers were
reporting on a sequence yet to come, or one which had
passed. Under the rules of this study, the judges called
these answers wrong; but even with these counted out, the
numerical results were extraordinary.

This test series conducted by Mrs. Moss is an example of
the modern ESP experimentation being conducted in psychology laboratories all over the world. Some scientists such
as Drs. T. D. Duane and T. Behrendt of the Jefferson Medical College, Philadelphia, Pennsylvania, have reported finding ESP induced correlation between the electroencephalo-
grams of certain identical twins. Others at Duke University
have studied the relationship between anxiety proneness and
ESP scoring (high ESP went with low defensiveness). Separation distance, I.Q., memory, skin resistance: all of these
have been probed in ESP tests. This modern experimentation
had its origin in the work and methods established by Dr.
Rhine at Duke in the 1930s. More than any other man, he
organized ESP testing into a scientific pursuit.

Dr. Joseph Banks Rhine was born at Waterloo, Pennsylvania, on September 29, 1895. He took his graduate work
in biology at the University of Chicago, and received his
Ph.D. in 1925. Shortly afterwards, he joined the faculty of
the psychology department at Duke University in Durham,
North Carolina. Professor William McDougall, a British
psychologist who first taught at Harvard, set up the department at Duke. Dr. Rhine and his wife, Louisa, came to Duke

to study under Professor McDougall, to evaluate a large collection of notes taken at sittings with mediums. The problem of survival after death quickly gave way to the question of how a medium might obtain information from extrasensory sources. The first tests with clairvoyance and telepathy showed that strict precautions and sophisticated statistical analysis would be required to obtain meaningful results. The researchers knew they had something really important when, in the fall of 1933, one subject hit a twice-chance score in a clairvoyancy test. The mathematical probability of such a score being due to chance was absurdly remote. To the ESP workers, this was a demonstration of information transfer without the use of the senses. These tests were the subject of the first paper of the Duke group: *Extra Sensory Perception;* it was published in 1934 by the Boston Society for Psychical Research.

Although this monograph was not designed to appeal directly to the public, *The New York Times* gave it a rousing review. This apparently catalyzed a new wave of interest in ESP and popular articles, books, and radio programs based on the phenomena were soon appearing. This interest led Dr. Rhine to become extremely conservative about the releases made by Duke concerning his work; he permitted reports on his published data only.

The popularization of the Duke work led to another reaction: opposition of segments of the scientific community. Of this, Dr. Rhine says:

> . . . (There was) surprising vigor in the hostile reaction of a number of psychologists. They were undoubtedly shocked by the sensational publicity over these revolutionary findings. They could not know that all the public excitement was as much a surprise to the Duke workers as it was to them and that the publicity was a product of public interest in

the findings, not of any promotion given to publicizing them.

As a consequence, a few men who would have felt only a tolerant pity for the parapsychologist, venturing so far out of the range of orthodoxy, boiled up for a time in a towering rage of denunciation of the national craze they thought must have been deliberately generated and whipped up by irresponsible sensationalism. It was an atmosphere so acrid and clouded by the smoke of dissension as not to permit a calm judgement of the real merits of the findings presented. Criticisms were overdone, phrased in intemperate language, and published far too easily and incautiously.

Duke stuck by Dr. Rhine during this period of controversy and did not yield to the internal or external pressures which cried for the termination of his work.

The major criticisms against Dr. Rhine's experiments have been these: first, lack of clinical control permitted the correct answer to be known somehow by the subject or allowed the experimenter, subconsciously perhaps, to affect the data; and second, the mathematics used to evaluate the statistical significance was not sufficiently sophisticated or was simply wrong. The mathematical attack came first, and is not yet over. There was a crucial meeting of the American Institute of Mathematical Statistics, at Indianapolis in December 1937, in which the techniques being used for the analysis of the experiments were reviewed. Conclusion: general endorsement for the mathematical approach. However, as recently as June 1965, D. H. Rogosin, a psychologist in the Los Angeles City Schools, speaking at the UCLA symposium on ESP, said that probability theory cannot be used to prove the existence of anything not proved otherwise. A man can be sure to hit a target if there are enough of them out there. Statistical mathematics is still relatively new and for this reason he felt that another review of ESP was in order by the experts. Mr. Rogosin does not believe in ESP. He thinks it will be remembered as being in the inauspicious group of scientific mistakes and "intellectual diseases," ranking no better than astrology and phrenology. He said, "ESP is an ancient superstition, but in a scientific age, it is presented as science, instead of the science-fiction it really is . . . We cannot disregard the traditional concepts of cause and effect and reverse them . . . just because Rhine uses his own variety of inductive imagination."

In 1937 sets of poorly printed ESP cards appeared on the market for use in parlor games. These cards bore the approval and copyright of Dr. Rhine. Now his critics had something to fall on. His subjects, they said, had been simply receiving sensory cues from the cards themselves. But Dr. Rhine pointed out, in serious experiments, the cards were concealed from the subject either behind an opaque screen or even by the separation of walls since the subject and experimenter were in separate rooms in some cases.

This matter came to a head in another crucial meeting in September 1938, when the American Psychological Association conducted a round table between three proponents and opponents of ESP. The evidence was debated in emotion-charged sessions which Dr. Rhine recalls as tests "of the very right of these ESP workers to continue their researches." There appeared to be general agreement that the precautions being taken were adequate. Nevertheless, after this session the precautions against sensory cues and inaccuracy in recording were tightened. And with this tightened security, the results declined but were still very significant. The critics say: "See, the results declined when you took more precautions!" Yet even with the precautions, the results seem to remain significant. There was the implication that further refinement might make the results completely random, but no one could suggest any further precautions. To Dr. Rhine all of the tedious precautions removed some of the fun, some of the spontaneity, but the results of the experiments, according to him, can now hardly be doubted.

Yet, clearly, doubt still exists. In 1935 a survey was made of academic psychologists in this country, to determine their attitudes toward the validity of ESP research. Only a small minority answered that they believed the research to be valid. The major objections today lie still in the implicit criticism of the use of inadequate controls. A scientist might put it this way: many cases of supposed ESP do not stand up under close scrutiny. Probe deep enough and you may find honest mistakes, or simple fraud. Those few cases which cannot be explained immediately, could probably be understood also, if scientists were to investigate them more completely. But most scientists do not wish to waste their time on projects that seem so certain to be valueless. Since ESP seems to be so far outside the framework of causality on which the framework of physical science rests, much decisive evidence will be required before science will permit a restructuring of its most revered tenets. Physical science works well enough today without ESP; why change it?

When I asked his colleagues what kind of a man Dr. Rhine is, they used words such as: authoritarian, driver, energetic, leader. He is now devoting his energies toward the establishment of the Foundation for Research on the Nature of Man. This private institution is dedicated to the exploration and discovery of the ultimate capabilities of man. The first research unit in the Foundation will be the Institute for Parapsychology, which will inherit much of the property, staff and philosophy from the Duke Parapsychology Laboratory, which will be closed. *The Journal of Parapsychology,* once published by the Duke group, will be published by the

Institute; the Duke files on spontaneous ESP cases will also be transferred. Funding comes from private sources; the Foundation hopes to have $5,000,000 by December 1967. Its objectives extend beyond ESP research and it is intended that other institutes be established to probe the "territory of what identifies man."

Troubles and doubts notwithstanding, prophecy, clairvoyance, and telepathy may be necessary for our everyday business. When an executive makes a decision he weighs such facts as are presented to him, and then, based on his judgment, decides which way his corporation will proceed. Dr. William Wolf, of the University of Southern California Business School, has asked executives how they make decisions. Frequently they admit that they follow their judgment. More than once Dr. Wolf has seen decisions made contrary to the facts presented by assorted accountants and engineers. When asked why, the president or vice-president or board of directors, as the case may be, say they *felt* it was right. What is this but precognition, prophecy? What is this but intuition? Perhaps it is based on experience, perhaps on a private unverbalized evaluation of the credibility of the advisers; whatever the criteria, those that move properly, succeed. Have you ever known someone who simply could not make a correct decision? Perhaps he was lacking in the esoteric hormone or neuron connections that enhance his precognition or clairvoyance.

Many medical doctors will admit that some of their diagnoses are based on *feel* rather than some demonstrable fact. Perhaps they are exhibiting a little of Edgar Cayce when they say, "Mr. Jones, the trouble with your liver is thus and so . . ." Certainly there are some definitive tests which make diagnosis a mechanical chore, but more often than not, diagnosis must be based on some insight of the physician.

An experimenter in a Midwestern university is attempting to set up a computer diagnosis system for heart disease. As an input to the computer, he uses electrocardiograms. The computer analyzes the cardiograms and from the wiggles, squeaks, and bumps determines a proper diagnosis, prognosis, and treatment. In order to determine the proper diagnosis for a given cardiogram trace, the experimenter selected a panel of many noted heart specialists. He presented several different electrocardiogram traces to the individual panel members in the privacy of their own offices. The doctors gave their judgment of the character of the disease, its probable outcome and its proper treatment. The experimenter thus had the ability to compare the evaluation of experts given the same "input" data. He found that perhaps 50% of the doctors agreed on traces showing common disorders, which is encouraging. Only 2% of the doctors, he felt, were simply incompetent. Yet, when the doctors were given an electrocardiogram which they had diagnosed earlier, but without being told that it was a repeat test, only 60% gave the same evaluation. This inability to lock onto pat interpretations of discrete data caused the experimenter most of his trouble. It certainly illustrates that diagnosis is a matter of judgment, and perhaps intuition. The moral is this: if you find a doctor you trust, one who is most often right in his diagnosis, keep him.

So we see that, although it is not generally recognized, our quantified world may indeed be functioning now with the partial help of ESP. And if it could be expanded and understood, what would we have? Politicians would be honest because the people would know their real motives. Furthermore, they would want to be honest and seek those solutions which would be most beneficial to the world since only these would enhance their own power. Power itself would be a result of the exactness of their own ESP abilities. The ends which the people of the world seek, for all, more and better, would become the only valid reasons for government. There could be no such thing as political miscalculation or escalation, that is, the situation where a government mis-judges the motives of another and so produces a response unanticipated by the originator of the situation. There could be no covert war plans, no scheming, no treachery, no revo-lution.

If the ability to read minds comes on man in steps, for example through the use of hypnosis or a mind-stimulating drug, the world may be in for a very bad time. As in Orwell's *1984*, an omniscient police force isn't a very pretty thing to contemplate. This ability could be used not only to prevent crime through pre-execution discovery, but also to control and direct, to herd and stifle initiative.

The scientist would be able to penetrate his problem and discover nature through direct communication, so to speak. ESP would open to the scientist a new means of perception. He would know what is needed, and how to get there. Better than that, he might know the results of his work and its effect on civilization before he brings it to fruition.

Business could not exist in its present format. Every new advertising campaign would be known ahead of time by the competition. Worse perhaps, every false claim would be laid bare to the people. The innocent could no longer be seduced.

Impending disasters would simply not occur. Before an airplane lost its compressor blades or main spar, the pre-cognitive chief mechanic would sense the problem and fix it. If he did not, the passengers wouldn't fly anyway.

Hidden minerals would no longer be hidden. Gold, ura-nium, diamonds would be there for all who had the resources and cared to gather them. Water and oil divination would no longer be a trick for sorcerers.

Marriages would all be made in heaven, presumably. ESP could tell of the risks, the arguments, the heartbreaks, or of the love and contentment lurking in the simple selection of a mate.

Or universal ESP could be the greatest force of destruction man has ever known. It could destroy us as a race, both morally and physically. When we read an outwardly pleasant "Good morning" of a co-worker as an expression of hate and hypocrisy, will we be better off?

Is anyone working to bring ESP to a level of everyday practicality? Perhaps. In a newspaper article headlined: *RUSSIANS SEE TELEPATHY AS GUIDE OUT IN SPACE,* reporter Norma Lee Browning told of research in telepathy going on today in Russia. The scientists with whom she spoke felt that Dr. Rhine's tests were "very boring" and "proof of nothing of scientific value." Their objective is the practical mastering of the phenomena of thought transference. They hope to be able to use such mastery, they say, in communications with, for example, an alien race, or cosmonauts far out in space. Professor Leonid L. Vasiliev, head of Leningrad University's physiology department, calls his work "long distance suggestion." The article states:

> . . . Vasiliev claims to have mastered long ago the techniques of verbal suggestion in hypnosis. No longer need he say aloud to the subject: "Go to sleep. You are falling, falling, falling. Now you are asleep."
> He merely thinks or wills the subject into a hypnotic trance. He calls it "non-verbal" suggestion. And he can do it from a distance with the subject in another room or even in a distant city.
> Vasiliev demonstrated this—at least to the satisfaction of Soviet scientists—in experiments conducted jointly with ex-

perts from Bechterev Institute and using patients suffering predominantly from hysteria . . .

The subject, unaware of the nature of the experiment, was instructed only to press (a) balloon rhythmically. At a certain moment unknown to the subject, Vasiliev transmitted the mental order, "Go to sleep" and later, the order "wake up. . . ."

In 260 such experiments, the subjects in only 10% failed to respond to the mental hypnotizing or awakening . . .

Vasiliev believes telepathic transmission is accomplished by "some kind of energy, or factor so far unknown, yet belonging to the highest state of development of matter, i.e., to the substance and structure of the brain." To discover such energy or factor, he maintains, would be "tantamount to the discovery of nuclear energy."

Here's one reason for the interest which lies beyond communication with cosmonauts. A Rand Corporation study conducted in 1964, suggested the possibility of two fearful future weapons systems. These were: first, mass-hypnotic recruitment of forces from the population of the enemy; and second, mind reading. The exact form of this later possibility was not specified, but it could be in the nature of an advanced intelligence system, or perhaps more insidiously, as a "Big Brother" Orwellian domestic security check. The panelists who participated in this study believed that both systems would be quite effective, but, they agreed, at the present time neither seemed to be very feasible.

If Dr. Rhine and his fellow researchers are right, ESP exists. The fact that it conflicts with a large body of today's deterministic science is unfortunate, but if the phenomena are real, someday, somehow, they will fit in with our idea of the physical world. And someday, somehow, as we learn more, we will come to use and perhaps, I sincerely hope, even benefit from our new knowledge.

# COMMERCIAL
# RESURRECTION

There is a man among us who says immortality may be possible. He is R. C. W. Ettinger of Oak Park, Michigan. There is a good chance that what he claims may be true.

Life is a tenuous, frail, delicate breath, which, blown gently into inert and cold molecules, gives existence and peculiar individuality. It is not always easy to distinguish between the living and the lifeless. Life in simple bodies can be recognized by growth, movement, reproduction and metabolism; life in human beings by the beating of the heart, breathing, neural response, and love and hate or an occasional laugh or tear. In the absence of these the human is dead.

But the word *dead* is an inexact term. At death, all bodily functions do not stop simultaneously; death is a process rather than a singular event. This process can sometimes be reversed by quick medical action. We have all heard of almost drowned persons, whose heartbeat and breathing had stopped, being revived by mouth-to-mouth resuscitation. Heart attack victims have been revived by heart massage. These life-after-approximate-death occurrences are common enough.

Death proceeds from the cessation of certain gross functions of the body to final and ultimate cellular deterioration. For several minutes after the heart stops circulating blood through the body, the cells live, and reinstatement of circulation can and has brought bodily life back.

With the idea in mind that death is not usually an instantaneous event, R. C. W. Ettinger has suggested arresting the process of death and cellular deterioration just after the heart has stopped beating by specially preparing and then rapidly cooling the body. Stored cold, in this state of suspended death, further deterioration would be minimized. Years later, when suitable medical expertise had developed and the cause of death could be cured, the patient would be warmed. Biologically, he would be hardly older than when he died. New appropriate medical attention could be applied to the patient, and, in theory, he could be revived. A dying-dead-revived person would thus appear to travel forward in time, losing the years in which medical science could not cure him, effectively gaining immortality.

Mr. Ettinger has proposed this plan seriously and is the leader of a growing movement to implement it. Immortality is his trade.

Imagine yourself in a world twenty-five years hence. Cemeteries are rarely used. The un-dead are waiting in what we could call cold storage warehouses, built in subdued good taste on the outskirts of town. Medical research is devoted not only to saving lives, but to repairing the cold-sleeping. Funeral directors have become especially respected professionals since they now prepare the recently dead for their trip into time. Perhaps their name has changed since "funeral director" raises images not as clean and pure as demanded by the happy and pleasant un-death of their patients. What are they called? Let's guess: Doctors of Cryogenic Storage. Their degree: D.C.St.

Death, real death, is only for fools, only for those who carelessly die away from the D.C.St.'s with their quick freeze equipment. Beatniks, or their future equivalent, no longer joke about "blowing their cool." First aid boxes all have portable coolers. The Red Cross has courses in death saving. There are, of course, suicidal maniacs who refuse cold storage when they die; nothing can really be done with these psychotics except, possibly, force-freezing. A criminal, sentenced to die for his crimes, lives out his life knowing that eternity has escaped him. He will not be granted freezing unless special amnesty is received in time from the governor.

The church, of course, has a serious problem. They can no longer promise immortality in return for the good life. People would rather gamble on the progress of the medical profession than to go after the two birds in the bush promised by their pastors. The promise of last reward has lost its remaining credibility. Perhaps, to preserve continuity, D.C.St.'s will also be required to take minor courses in divinity, a prerequisite to the dispensing of eternity. When someone dies and is stored, there are no bereaved next of kin, no words of sympathy, only: "Lucky stiff. I wonder what year he's heading for?"

There are also those malcontents who, finding no pleasure

in the present, seek escape into the future. The operation to place them in storage is illegal, but authorities suspect it is widely practiced. Very accurate data are hard to accumulate except in Japan where the operation has been legalized by the government as a further measure toward reducing overcrowding and easing their food problems.

In this world, twenty-five years from now, the steps required to prepare the un-dead for their journey in time are not mysterious. Mr. Ettinger has already described them today. As soon as possible after death, the temperature of the body should be decreased to about 10 degrees C. There are only minutes to spare, so this should be accomplished quite quickly; one method would be to simply pack the body in ice or surround it in mattresses in which ice water circulates. During this time the circulation of oxygenated blood should be maintained. This after-death circulation can be accomplished through the use of a heart-lung machine or a closed chest resuscitator. These resuscitators are in wide use today by fire departments and life-saving services throughout the country. Then, when the body has reached 10 degrees C., its blood must be withdrawn and replaced with a protective solution. Ettinger suggests using dimethyl sulfoxide preferably, or, lacking this, glycerine. This fluid should be introduced into an artery as the blood is drawn off through a vein. It can be injected using a hang bottle, the heart lung machine itself, or an embalmer's pump if the pressure is not too high.

Once the blood has been removed, the temperature of the body can be lowered to its storage point, minus 197 degrees C. This temperature is attainable using liquid nitrogen which can be readily purchased in high pressure cylinders from companies that specialize in the manufacture of commercial gases. After the body has chilled to minus 197 degrees C. it will be placed in its storage box for its trip through time. The box, of course, must be specially prepared to maintain this low temperature. Mr. Ettinger envisions the time when large public installations will be available, providing low temperature storage for all at reasonable cost, perhaps through Social Security.

Mr. Ettinger wrote a book in 1964, *The Prospect of Immortality,* in which he explained the details of the preservation of bodies and explored the implications of this practice from personal, moral, religious and legal views. The book raises and attempts to answer questions such as: Does memory survive freezing? Can a wife remarry if her husband is frozen? What happens to the estate of a time traveling body?

I wrote to Mr. Ettinger and asked him about the history of his book. He told me that the idea for freezing first occurred to him in 1947, when he was a patient in the Percy Jones (Army) Hospital in Battle Creek, Michigan. He had read about some experiments in freezing and revival of animal tissue and incorporated these ideas in a science-fiction short story, "The Penultimate Trump," which appeared in *Startling Stories* in March 1948. The hero of the story was frozen alive, that is, put into suspended animation, but he would have been frozen after death if the more advanced techniques were not worked out in time. For the next twelve years, Mr. Ettinger did not pursue the idea beyond talking with family and friends; he felt all along that someone with more prestige would surely implement the idea. Finally, in 1960, he wrote up the concept very briefly, emphasizing the insurance aspects, and contacted one hundred people or so selected at random from Who's Who. There were few answers: clearly more detail was needed. Mr. Ettinger wrote a first draft of his book, *The Prospect of Immortality* in the summer of 1962 and sent copies to people who he believed could offer informed comment. According to Mr. Ettinger, McGraw-Hill turned this first manuscript down "after great initial interest, because they felt it wouldn't fill a book—it was short, and included some material of doubtful relevance." Then Dr. Jean Rostand, a French scientist who has conducted many experiments with frozen animal tissue, agreed to write one of the prefaces to the book. Some revisions were made, and Doubleday agreed to publish it after they received comments from their prepublication reviewers. The freezer movement, for better or worse, had started.

Mr. Ettinger was born in 1918 and served in the 1st Infantry Division during World War II. He was wounded in Germany in 1944 and spent the next three years in Army hospitals. He was retired, finally, in 1948 as a first lieutenant. After the war, Mr. Ettinger completed his education, receiving Bachelor of Science, Master of Science and Master of Arts degrees from Wayne State University in Detroit, Michigan. He then taught physics, physical sciences, mathematics, and astronomy at Wayne State, Lawrence Institute of Technology, and Highland Park College. Currently Mr. Ettinger is on a one-year sabbatical from Highland Park. He lives in Oak Park, Michigan, a quiet town near Detroit, with his wife and two children, and is devoting full time to the cryogenic interment project.

Mr. Ettinger has written that not "a single scientific error of any consequence has been pointed out" since the publication of his book. Yet in its review of *The Prospect of Immortality*, *Science* said:

> . . . One may take this kind of thing seriously or one may not. If one does, the book can only be considered the work of an utterly confused optimist . . . Only such a man could quote people so uncritically and so out of context . . .

There is absolutely no evidence that low temperature
storage and recovery procedures will be possible in the near
future with live human beings, let alone dead ones . . .
Perhaps the author has been pulling our legs. Maybe it's
science fiction after all . . .

Mr. Neil P. Ruzic, editor of the respected technical journal
*Industrial Research,* says that it is doubtful if Ettinger will
find support for the freeze plan because, "all investigators
in the field of reduced metabolism consider his proposal
preposterous." I asked Mr. Ettinger for his view of these
statements. He furnished me with a list of scientists who
support his proposal, some privately—others in print. The
*Science* reviewer had called him "utterly confused." He used
the same term for the reviewer. ". . . He (the reviewer)
missed the point completely, since it is central to my proposal that we do not need recovery procedures in the near
future." Mr. Ettinger continued, criticizing Ruzic's critique.
"(His) quoted remark is irresponsible not only with respect
to the word 'all' but also the word 'preposterous'; the pre-
vailing expert view is that the program is premature, . . .
but this is a long way from regarding it as 'preposterous.'"

A panel of experts at RAND were asked to predict possible
scientific accomplishments that might occur in the next fifty
years. While there was not complete agreement, the group
felt that there was a chance that some sort of time-travel
might be possible after the turn of the century, through an
artificially induced coma leading effectively to a state of
nonaging hibernation of the human body. Mr. Ettinger believes that suspended animation, that is suspended life, will
also come, but suspended death can be practiced now; in
fact it is the greatest folly not to practice it now.

There already has been much experimentation with freezing organisms, storing them at low temperatures and then

warming them back to life. Sperm cells have been stored for years and then successfully used in artificial insemination experiments. Dr. Jerome K. Sherman of the University of Arkansas has conducted many frozen-sperm tests with animals and in an epic demonstration of the technique successfully inseminated two women with human sperm which had been stored for two months at liquid nitrogen temperatures. Success with this type of research has led physicist Ralph E. Lapp to urge that we build a sperm bank so that a nonmutated supply would be available in its shielded vaults in the event of nuclear war. Some scientists have frozen rabbit ova, and then fertilized them after thawing. They plan to continue their work with human ova.

In a limited way, experimentation is progressing all over the world. Professor Isamu Suda of Kobe University, Tokyo, is reported to have frozen a cat's brain for several months and obtained a normal encephalogram when it was thawed; another scientist, Professor Simon Ostrach of Case Institute of Technology, Cleveland, Ohio, has developed a proprietary freezing method for a private company which is said to cause far less damage.

Even if Ettinger's whole body freezing plan cannot be developed, it appears that human genetic material, at least, can be stored and revitalized for later use. The stored ova can be implanted in substitute mothers or perhaps fertilized *in vitro* a la Huxley's *Brave New World,* to develop from ova to embryo to fetus in a glass womb. Recent experimentation even suggests that an ovum or sperm cell might be tricked into self-reproduction, autogenesis, so that the resulting individual would be a twin of the donor. This is almost Ettinger's immortality, but not quite, since the twin would have an ego of his own, and death would still be death to the donor.

In his book Mr. Ettinger cites research conducted with quick frozen organs which, when thawed, were implanted successfully; microscopic animals that lived after dehydration, freezing, storage, and warming; the larvae of an insect which progressed to their next development stage after freezing and warming; embryo chicken hearts which were treated with a glycerol solution, frozen and then resumed beating when warmed; rats and dogs that under certain circumstances were cooled to the freezing point and survived. Nevertheless, mammals have not been frozen, stored and thawed successfully. While much experimental work has been done, a great deal more remains. How much damage occurs in freezing; is the brain adversely affected; what is the proper storage temperature; how long can a body be stored? What procedures are best? Ettinger certainly doesn't say these problems have been solved. He merely says they *will* be solved, someday, and we ought to preserve and store bodies by the best methods available to us today. Someday medical science may be able to repair the cause of death, and whatever damage is done in freezing. The chance of this happening, he reasons, is better than the other alternative, decay.

Damage occurs in several ways during the freezing of cells. The various organic solutions within the cells will, of course, form ice crystals when their freezing temperatures have been reached. These crystals occupy more volume than the solutions which formed them. This expansion can pierce the membranes of the cells. When these solutions freeze, first water forms ice. The concentration of the remaining fluids increases and this may cause chemical damage. The freezing also causes mechanical shrinkage at varying rates and this causes stresses which may be damaging to the cellular materials. Even though storage at liquid nitrogen temperatures greatly inhibits any chemical reactions, some will proceed slowly. These could only be prevented by lowering the temperature even further, down to close to absolute zero. The problems experienced in freezing are encountered again in thawing: unless ice crystals go back into solution quickly and essentially simultaneously, the cell can again be damaged mechanically and chemically. Mr. Ettinger points out that new heating devices such as microwave diathermy offer promise here. The problem is not simple. But, perhaps, as Mr. Ettinger reasons, when medicine can cure the diseases of the frozen non-dead it can also repair the damage incurred in freezing and thawing.

How far has the movement gone? Pretty far. Offer people a chance to keep their precious egos forever and you've started a new industry. Paradise is nothing compared to a half promise of rebirth.

The Life Extension Society, 2011 N Street, N.W., Washington, D.C., is a scientifically oriented, nonprofit, nonsalaried corporation. It has issued "freeze cards" to subscribers, instructing physicians on the proper methods of preparation of the bearer's body.

The Cryonics Society of New York, 103–55 97th Street, Ozone Park, New York, is also a nonprofit organization which intends to set up facilities for processing and storage.

Juno, Inc., an Ohio firm, has built and tested cryogenic caskets, "time capsules." They plan to sell their product to funeral directors and cemetery operators. Production is starting this year.

Cryolife Corporation, 2727 Main Street, Kansas City, Missouri, is preparing to offer a complete package deal, including preparation and storage.

Continuelife Corporation, 131 Avenue C, Latrobe, Pennsylvania, is reported to be acquiring facilities.

Cryo-Care Equipment Corporation, 2204 W. Indian School Road, Phoenix, Arizona, has designed and built an aluminum two-man cryogenic interment capsule, according to its director, E. F. Hope (an appropriate name for this new business). The capsule should sell for about $3200; its liquid nitrogen will cost about $50 a year, according to Mr. Ettinger.

Immortality may be a salable commodity.

Funeral directors will probably agree that cryogenic storage is a good thing. A reporter at a three-day convention of Ohio funeral directors in Columbus, Ohio, asked if people would really pay for this service.

"Sure, people will pay. They'll do it on time payment plans," was the answer. Ettinger himself says that funeral directors will "enjoy universal esteem." He pictures the funeral home of the near future providing necessary preparation, initial freezing and temporary storage. Longer duration storage of "time capsules" would be in specially insulated mausoleums, plumbed for quick liquid nitrogen hook-up. It just occurs to me that this is an area in which our space program can make significant contribution. We can look to our sophisticated space vehicles for high performance insulation; quick disconnects, leakproof and nonjamming; for means of producing large quantities of liquid nitrogen; and the advanced components associated with cryogenic handling techniques.

To my knowledge, at this writing, there has been only one attempt to put Mr. Ettinger's ideas into practice. UPI covered the story with an article headlined: *PATIENT'S DEATH HALTS FREEZER CAPSULE TEST:*

> . . . A plan for the first scientific effort to place a human body in a state of suspended death for a number of years was abandoned Thursday.

A man who had planned to have his dying wife entombed upon her death cancelled the experiment.

A spokesman for the City Hospital said the plan was abandoned because the woman's condition had improved slightly during the night and upon advice of her pastor.

Shortly after the experiment was abandoned, the woman died of a heart and lung ailment . . .

The board of City Hospital held an emergency meeting late Wednesday night and vetoed any plan for its staff to cooperate in the project . . .

The woman's husband arranged with an area volunteer fire department to pick up the body and administer artificial respiration for the few minutes it would take to put it into the freezer capsule.

A large number of scientists and newsmen had flown into Springfield (Ohio) hoping to see the event.

The hospital announcement said the woman's pastor made a statement that religious beliefs were not involved but pointed out there was no law regulating such matters. He also said several doctors advised the husband they could not give him any encouragement as to restoring the woman to active life at some future date.

The experiment was to have been performed on a woman whose husband had read Ettinger's book. A story in the *National Enquirer* contained an interview with him in which he discussed his motivations in attempting to freeze his wife's body.

. . . I loved her dearly and wanted to keep that love alive. I tried desperately to find a doctor who could cure her heart disease. When I was finally told there was no chance, I asked the doctors if there might be a chance 10 or 20 years from now, when surgical techniques have been further improved. The doctors said yes, there might be a chance. And that's when I decided I would try to preserve my wife's body. I hoped that one day the doctors could revive her and then perform heart surgery.

According to the article, he called Mr. Ettinger and they, together with Leonard Gold, president of Juno, Inc., set about to plan the experiment. Juno was to furnish the capsule; Mr. Ettinger was to supervise the freezing operation. In the end, it was the hospital which prevented the preservation, because, the article said, "they were worried about the legality of preserving a body this way."

The Reverend Kay Glaesner of St. John's Evangelical Lutheran Church had the pioneering role of advising whether to freeze the woman's body. He advised the family that, from a religious standpoint, freezing was permissible. Several weeks later he delivered a sermon which clearly stated his philosophy and perhaps anticipates the philosophy of organized religion.

> Christianity cannot object to the art of rejuvenation . . . Life could be extended a year, one hundred years, or a thousand years, but there is still no doubt in the minds of thinking people that such . . . is but a small span in the totality of God's plan. Any art or craft of man will not evade or nullify the judgement of God. Life now and forevermore remains within the Providence of God. We shall resurrect whether in the body, in the grave, or in the frozen casket . . .

The church, as it has many times in the past, may be able to adapt, and adaptation is the key to survival.

This experiment was abandoned, but the pattern it established is clear. People will want to hold on to their loved ones or their own beloved egos. They may want this hold out of affection, out of guilt, out of fear. Since you can't take it with you anyway, what better way to spend your money than to take a chance on eternity?

Ettinger has abstracted from early scientific experiments a social concept based on the mutability of death. He is ahead of science as were Reverend Loehr and Dr. Rhine. He is conjecturing in an area which has not yet been articulated by science, the church, or society. I don't know whether he is right. It would seem that the most effective argument would be the successful freezing and resuscitation of a laboratory animal, perhaps a chimpanzee. A demonstration such as this might herald a new way of death.

In his book Ettinger has carried his case directly to the public. He feels that once the public accepts the plan, science will follow. Perhaps they can force the social revolution which he proposes, but I doubt it. I am inclined to think, rather, that the revolution must be first sanctioned by science; until then it will not get funding or even a friendly nod from government, or the medical or legal professions. If the pattern we have found is followed, perhaps a graduate student or a young scientist, working in a discipline not too closely allied with the field in which he was trained, will perform the crucial chimpanzee experiment. He will write papers and publish wherever he can. All of those scientists and doctors who have had their toes stepped on will call, "foul—bad laboratory procedures." Perhaps others will say, "It's not right to be frozen." Gradually the new idea may sweep by the old staked reputations, creating new disciplines, new university chairs, new professions and a new divinity if necessary, in its wake.

This may not be the future of commercial resurrection. An idea which is not viable simply peters out along the way. But Ettinger has his own advice to the doubters:

. . . To each his own, and to those who choose not to be frozen, all I can say is—rot in good health . . .

(10

# THE
# HOLES
# IN
# YOUR HEAD

Couldn't sleep last night. Who can before a dentist's appointment? Here it is, nine A.M. already.

"Hello, Mr. Schwartz, go right in."

"Thank you, Miss Nurse," I say.

Why no wait this morning? She's smiling at me. Something's wrong. He probably has a golf game lined up this afternoon and wants to get out of here in a hurry. Maybe there's a little hanky-panky going on with the nurse. She's not so bad, you know.

There's the seat, scientifically contoured to absorb my pain. The nurse is still smiling and I'm smiling back like a patent idiot. God, that's a big bib she's tying on. Are they expecting me to hemorrhage?

"Hello there, Doctor." I can barely see his form out there in the murk beyond the beam.

"Hello, Mr. Schwartz. How are we feeling today?"

"We're feeling fine, just fine. Ha ha." I decide it's probably not in good taste to joke at a time like this. What's that thing he's got there in his hand? He brought it in in a felt-lined piccolo case. Is that a *needle?* He must have taken it home to sharpen. I can picture him at home, in his basement laboratory absorbed in his favorite pastime of sharpening his instruments.

Now he's looking at the little square X rays on the viewing plate. Miss Nurse, with whom he's obviously having an affair, I'm sure now, is over with him. Look at the two of them there. Bela Lugosi and Boris Karloff. What are they whispering about? They think I'm not watching. Whoops, they turned around. Look nonchalant. What can I look at? Up, that's it. Straight up.

Did you ever notice the Chinese water torture they turn on to distract you? It always happens about this time. The water dribbles into the cup and then overflows into the sterile, cold, black marble receptical, with a sound suggestive of a very natural body function. But can you get up? Do you even know where the bathroom is? If you could get up, would you with the two of them over there?

He's pointing at the X rays with his little bright mirror. I know what they're saying; "What a pity. He's so young to have a mouthful of rotted teeth. We'll have to amputate." They turn. He's got the piccolo case under his arm. They're both smiling now and touch elbows lightly.

What pretty teeth they have.

Is there an American who hasn't played his turn in the dentist's chair? Yet with all of the pain and discomfort, with all of the X rays, fluoridation, mouthwashes, dentifrices, toothbrushes, dental floss, and up-and-down, not right-and-left brushing, the cavities bore on, eroding enamel, respecting neither age nor class nor color. We have built a mystique, a cosmetology around teeth. We like them bright, odor free, and well aligned and often spend considerable amounts of money to insure that they remain in that condition.

Yet, alas, teeth still seem to rot.

Decay of the teeth is a disease known as caries. The actions we take to prevent caries are, in fact, disease preventives. Has the prophylaxis of any other illness in the United States received more attention, money, and advertising time? From the standpoint of our general awareness and the preventive measures we take, caries must be the number one disease in the United States today.

With all of this awareness, you'd think *they'd* do something about cavities, wouldn't you? But who are *they*? What are *they* doing? Surrounding these questions is a little known controversy which penetrates to the nerve, so to speak, of the structure of scientific sociology, to the core of the problem of promulgation of ideas which buck the tide of established opinion. The fate of our teeth and our children's teeth may be immutably determined by the outcome of this conflict of ideas.

Dentistry is not a very old profession. Prior to 1800, barbers performed oral surgery. The red stripe in the barber pole derives its color from this aspect of the tonsorial art. Blacksmiths were responsible for extractions, using the crude but effective wrought-iron tools of the trade. Silversmiths and jewelers made bridges to fill the gaps between missing teeth. Man's trouble with his teeth predates these practitioners, however. It apparently extends back to the beginnings of civilization. Hippocrates and Aristotle referred to dental operations in their writings; Egyptian mummies have been found with artificial teeth fabricated of wood, ivory, bone, or stone. There is even some evidence that they used gold for fillings.

In 1840, the year that the world's first dental college was chartered in Baltimore, the American Society of Dental Surgeons was formed. Its short history illustrates the trap into which professional societies can fall. The organization was apparently destined for a long and prosperous life; it had its own *Journal;* its officers were respected dentists; its members saw themselves as an emerging professional elite. In the early 1840s, shortly after the society organized, the Crawcour brothers arrived in New York from France and advertised a novel filling material, a mercury amalgam, which they called Royal Mineral Succedaneum. This material was offered as a replacement for gold. Their methods were apparently successful, and legitimate dentists of the area, including prominent officers of the society, began to feel the pinch of competition. Many dentists, believing that mercury compounds were injurious to the patient and interested in surviving economically, declared open warfare and attacked amalgam as detrimental to public health. The Frenchmen were forced to leave the country.

But even after the Crawcour brothers left, some dentists who had begun to use amalgam because of its low cost continued using it. The profession divided neatly into two camps; those who used it and "those who wouldn't be caught dead with it." According to historians, there were few scientific investigations into the suitability of amalgam from a health standpoint; instead, dentists belonged to one side or the other, each side dogmatically supporting its views. This was the amalgam war.

The "wouldn't-touch-it-with-a-ten-foot-pole" boys happened to be the "in" group of the society. A committee of that group was appointed to study the effect of mercury compounds on the body when used in fillings. They found that "all such articles were harmful both to the teeth and every part of the patient's mouth." On July 20, 1843, the society issued a proclamation: the use of amalgam was malpractice. Some of the members continued to use it regardless, particularly in filling the teeth of poorer patients. Then the society appointed a committee to enforce its position. Each member of the society was asked to sign the following pledge:

> . . . I hereby certify it to be my opinion and firm conviction that any amalgam whatever . . . is unfit for the plugging of teeth or fangs and I pledge myself never under any circumstances to make use of it in my practice, as a dental surgeon . . .

Every member had to sign or be expelled from the group. The dentists revolted. The issue now wasn't simply amalgam, it was freedom. By 1856 the group could no longer even muster a quorum to vote itself out of existence.

There followed a period of distrust of potentially dictatorial organizations. Gradually state units were built and some of these still survive. The American Dental Association is the major dental group in the United States today, of course, and is a powerful spokesman for the profession.

Theories about the causes of cavities must have originated at the time of the first toothache. Cavities have been ascribed to worms boring holes in the enamel as they were observed to do in wood, corrosive ill humors arising from abnormalities in the blood, and internal inflammation, among many other concepts which were, in their time, the "truth."

Aristotle thought there was a connection between sweets and cavities, and the Romans found a link between their confections and bad teeth. The idea that residual food particles and acids might be responsible for cavities was first postulated in the early 1800s, but full articulation of the acid theory came from the work of W. D. Miller, in 1890. He stated that tooth enamel was a very effective protection against decay since the enamel had to be penetrated somehow in order for the attack to progress to the inner portions of the tooth. His research was concerned with the method of penetration of the enamel, which he finally blamed on lactic acid that formed from the fermentation of food particles in the mouth. This acid, he reasoned, dissolved the enamel. Later it was found that mechanisms existed in the mouth that tended to keep the lactic acid in contact with the teeth under certain conditions, so the matter seemed proven, at least circumstantially.

The path to a cure seemed at hand. Simply keep the mouth clean. Get rid of the food particles. Get rid of the acid. So we have been taught to brush our teeth, cleaning agents have been invented, the great toothpaste industry has been created. But cavities continue. Adherents of Miller's theory, which is by far the majority of dentists, say simply that we haven't yet found a way to reach all of the particles of food through brushing. Gradually dental researchers are looking for other contributory factors. But acid is still king.

Cavities start in the enamel. This hard covering is a rather unique substance which is not yet completely understood. There is an organic matrix running throughout the enamel, a framework of protein molecules. This mesh surrounds and supports mineral crystals which provide the enamel with its white color, hardness, gloss and body. If the organic matrix and the mineral crystals exist as separate but intimate entities, the enamel's structure must resemble a peculiar kind of concrete, with the pebbles, the mineral crystals; and the cement, the organic matrix. It is possible that the protein and the calcium salts in the mineral crystals are actually chemically bonded at their interface. If this is so, the molecular structure of the enamel must be very complex indeed.

Most authorities today believe that an organic matrix of some form exists. Almost all contemporary studies have tended to confirm this concept of the structure of enamel. Yet, when it was first stated in 1905 by Dr. C. F. Bodecker, it was vigorously attacked and denied. For fifty years Dr. Bodecker persisted in his attempts to show his colleagues the real constitution and function of this complex material. He had trouble with this idea because, as in so many cases in this book, it bucked the establishment. Miller had articulated the acid theory of tooth decay twenty years before Bodecker's work. Enamel, simply, was a mineral structure and acid ate into that structure to initiate caries. If a protein network were present, then another possibility would have to be admitted: caries might result from an enzymatic attack on the protein rather than a dissolving action of acids on the calcium salts. This possibility was denied vigorously for fifty years. Yet today Bodecker is recognized for his work on the protein matrix as one of the few original contributors to dentistry.

No one doubts that caries involve the loss of calcium salts from the enamel of a tooth. The pro-acid group says that this decalcification comes from the attack of acid. The acid is produced by bacterial fermentation of carbohydrates in the mouth. This action is enhanced by the presence of sugar. Therefore, "cut down on sweets and brush after every meal if you want to reduce cavities." Experimental tests have been performed which would seem to confirm this position. Enamel from extracted teeth has been destroyed by acid in the laboratory; cariogenic subjects have shown high mouth acidity; germ-free rats appear to get cavities when their mouth acidity is high after they are inoculated with known species of bacteria.

"But," argues the other school, "this is circumstantial evidence at best. We will concede that acid can *erode* enamel. This does not establish it as the initiator of caries, only as an agent of erosion once decay has started. Furthermore, identification of the presence of acid in carie-prone subjects merely shows that acid is there. It does not indicate the mechanism of attack."

This other school goes by the imposing name of proteolysis-chelation. They contend that bacteria, acting on the protein in the tooth through a process known as proteolysis, produce not only acids, but many other compounds as well. Among these other compounds is a group of chemicals known as chelating agents. This word, chelate, comes from the Greek *chele* which means to grab or pinch in the sense of a crab claw. This is just what chelating agents do—pinch or grab on the molecular level, trying to absorb metal atoms within their structure. In its chemical definition, calcium is a metal, and these chelating agents in the mouth go after the calcium to fill in holes in their molecular structure.

Here then is the difference between the two schools: the acid school says bacterial fermentation of carbohydrates results in acids which can dissolve calcium salts under the proper conditions: the chelation school says that bacterial proteolysis results in chelating agents which decalcify. Sugar is cariogenic in both theories since it promotes the formation of acids as well as chelators, and fluoridation seems to retard both acid attack and chelation. So why all the fuss? These theories sound almost the same. But *acid inhibits chelation.* So the pro-chelators say that treatment which removes acid from the mouth does not prevent cavities, it promotes them.

The difference in view thus centers around the nature of the chemical reaction which initiates the attack on the enamel, but this is a wide and important scientific gulf.

After reading both theories, the venerated acid theory of Miller's and the proteolysis-chelation hypothesis, a non-initiated layman is tempted to say: "For crying out loud . . . I don't care who's right. All I know is I've got a toothache. If somebody, anybody has a new idea, please give it a try."

The concept of chelation is not in itself new and unique. This reaction in which a molecule grabs a metal atom into its microscopic bosom is well known to researchers in other fields. In soil formation, it is a chelation process which converts rocks into soil. Within soil, microbes produce chelating agents that convert minerals into soluble forms that can be absorbed by living plants.

It is understandable that a soil chemist would be intimately familiar with the process of chelation. Dr. Albert Schatz was trained as a soil chemist and soil microbiologist; he and his principal collaborator, Dr. Joseph Martin, D.D.S., have emerged as the leaders of the proteolysis-chelation theory of caries they invented. Dr. Schatz's early work with soil microbes led to the discovery of streptomycin. He and his collaborators first described this most important antibiotic in 1944. He came into dental research with impeccable credentials and much honor. His new thought was simply this: oral microbes can produce chelating agents in a manner similar to the action of microbes in the soil. These oral chelating chemicals may dissolve minerals in enamel in the same way they dissolve minerals in the soil. He has had great difficulty in conducting research and in publishing his work because, he feels, this simple idea is contrary to the opinion of most dentists. To them, acid is the culprit of caries. Reputations are at stake and there is no room for a new theory.

Dr. Schatz was born in 1920. He majored in soil science at Rutgers University and took his doctorate there in 1945 in soil microbiology. His dissertation dealt with streptomycin, an antibiotic which he codiscovered during his graduate research work, in the department of soil microbiology at this school. After he graduated, he worked as a biochemist for the New York State Department of Health, a microbiologist for the Sloan-Kettering Institute for Cancer Research, and as a research microbiologist for the Dental Research Laboratory of the Passaic General Hospital. He was Director of Research and Professor of Microbiology at the National Agricultural College. He was Chief of the Division of Microbiology of the Philadelphia General Hospital. He was a professor on the faculties of chemistry, pharmacy, medicine, and agronomy at the University of Chile in Santiago, Chile. He is currently on the faculty and conducting research at Washington University, St. Louis, Missouri. The scope of these prestigious assignments speaks for itself. Dr. Schatz has held many of them in parallel, working across disciplines to pursue fields of research which interested him. These fields have included: streptomycin and other antibiotics, fungi, pigments, industrial microbiology, protozoa, bacteriophage, animal viruses, chlorophyll, phosphate metabolism, vitamins, histologic techniques, lipid catabolism, atherosclerosis, soil sciences, education, history, dental caries, and many others. He is a Fellow of the Royal Society

for the Promotion of Health in Great Britain, and a member
of many other societies; was elected one of the "ten outstanding young men of 1953" by the United States Junior
Chamber of Commerce; and received the "Man of the Year"
award from the Drug and Allied Products Guild. He received a $4000 award for his work relating to the proteolysis-
chelation theory of dental caries, not from a dental society,
but from the Soil and Health Foundation. Dr. Schatz has
received honorary degrees from three universities, and has
been named an honorary member of several medical and
dental societies. His publications have been numerous, in
fact a concise list fills twelve pages. In short, Dr. Schatz is
a prolific and brilliant contributor in many fields.

Yet, when Drs. Schatz and Martin first articulated the
chelation theory, they could not publish in the United States.
The paper was titled *Chelation or Metal Binding as a New
Approach to the Problem of Dental Caries*. It finally ap-
peared in the Spanish periodical *Euclides*. Of this episode
Dr. Schatz says:

> . . . Our paper appeared in a European periodical since
> American journals refused to publish it. Three reasons were
> given for rejecting this manuscript which announced the
> chelation theory: (a) Acid had been *proved* to be the cause
> of tooth decay; (b) Enamel minerals could not possibly dis-
> solve in nonacid solutions; and (c) Chelation could not occur
> in living systems and therefore would be of no interest to
> dentistry.

To these claims Dr. Schatz says: all scientifically false. "This
illustrates what can happen (and does) when incompetent
people are placed in positions of authority."

One of his papers on proteolysis-chelation appeared in
the *Journal of the American Dental Association* in 1962.
This publication is, of course, the most prestigious voice of

American dentistry. But even here Schatz and Martin were faced with rejection by innuendo. The editor essentially instructed his readers to beware of this strange idea. His own personal comment was inserted over the article:

> Like all theories (proteolysis-chelation) will be subject to suspended judgment until it is fully substantiated . . .

With this kind of warning from authority, could the readers really evaluate the proposal objectively? Furthermore, as Dr. Schatz points out, when a theory is fully substantiated, it is no longer a theory, it is fact.

Reprints of this article also contained a footnote warning which disassociated the American Dental Association from "all expressions of opinion and all statements of supposed facts" which, the footnote writer said, were "published on the authority of the writer." Of course, who but the author of a new idea has responsibility for it?

Yet publishers have a responsibility to their readers. When a reader subscribes to a magazine he has some idea about what he will get in the months that follow. In this respect, *Science* and the *Journal of the American Dental Association* are no different than *Time* or *Life*. The magazines follow a set format and editorial policy. If the publisher and his staff select interesting and topical subjects, the periodical is viable; if not, circulation decreases. Stated simply, subscribers to scientific periodicals do not expect to see kook articles. If many papers appear that are judged *screwy* by the readers, circulation will decrease. Since the only justification, other than profit, for the existence of a scientific magazine is the dissemination of information to as wide an audience as possible, a declining circulation is clearly untenable. Therefore, it follows that papers are printed that agree with the basic tenets of the discipline involved. A journal on rocket propulsion might think twice about publishing an article about a theory of antigravity; acid is the mode of American dentistry. This is part of the dilemma.

Drs. Schatz and Martin publish most often in small dental journals such as the *Pakistan Dental Review,* and the *New York State Dental Journal.* I asked why. Dr. Schatz wrote me:

> . . . Small journals do not have, as a general rule, big shots on their editorial boards. So, they can afford the luxury of being open minded. The *big* journals have the *big shots* on their editorial boards. Naturally, these big boys are either authorities on caries from the acid point of view or if they are not directly interested in caries they sure as hell are not going to allow anything in print that will antagonize their friends who are pro-acid lads. So, the sort of stuff I publish can only be gotten into these other journals where the editors are in a position to be open minded.

Most of the people in this book have, at one time or another, found difficulty in being published. The pressure which Velikovsky's book received from eminent and respected scientists delayed his book, caused traumatic changes in publication houses, and eventually cast Velikovsky as an outsider. His case is not unique. Professor McConnell resorted to his *Worm Runner's Digest;* Professor Nagy had his problems too. The staid profession of dentistry does not escape this weapon of academic reactionism. Dr. Schatz tells of a significant example in his review of a new dental book titled *The Toxicology of Fluorine.* This book was a compendium of papers presented at a symposium held in Bern, Switzerland, in October 1962, dealing with the potentially poisonous aspects of fluoridation. This would seem to be a mild enough topic, certainly one deserving full scientific exposure. The question examined at the symposium was simply this: Is fluoridation dangerous? The lectures were delivered by scientists and medical doctors of the highest integrity and competence. Yet, Dr. Schatz wrote:

> . . . Neither the symposium nor the book received any support, financial or otherwise, from dental organizations. On the contrary, some such groups actively opposed both the meeting and publication of the report. Consequently, the two were carried out independently of the dental profession, despite the fact that dentistry is responsible for the controversy concerning toxic effects associated with fluoridation and is intimately involved in this problem.
>
> The symposium was originally scheduled to be held in Holland, but because of opposition from dental interests in that country it was transferred to Bern, Switzerland. There, others subsequently opposed publication of the book because it, like the symposium, would inevitably raise questions about the safety and wisdom of fluoridation (and about some who had initiated this program and were continuing it). There are powerful forces which now have a vested interest in perpetuating fluoridation because their reputations depend on its continuation . . .
>
> Two years elapsed between the 1962 symposium and publication . . . in 1964 because of the efforts that were made to suppress the book. For example, one publishing house, which puts out dental and medical literature, agreed to print *The Toxicology of Fluorine,* and invested some 10,000 Swiss francs in setting up the text in type. But it was then warned that if it went ahead and published this particular book the dental community would stop patronizing it. In the face of this threatened economic boycott and enticed by an offer of compensation to cover all expenses incurred, the publisher "dropped" the book.
>
> It is to the credit of the editor Dr. T. Gordonoff, Emeritus Professor of Pharmacology at the University of Bern, that he

> persisted for almost two years in the face of such unprece-
> dented discouragement and opposition . . .
> The book was finally published by Schwabe & Co. . . .

The question is clearly not only whether fluoridation is safe but whether our scientific reception system should inhibit free discussion of such an important matter.

An article written by Dr. Victor Daniels appeared in *The Journal of the American Dental Association* in which it was reported that Dr. Schatz had "announced" himself as "definitely against fluoridation" at a meeting on the prevention of caries in Chile. This announcement of his views, according to Dr. Schatz, had simply never taken place. In order to correct this statement and others in the article which he believed to be in error, Dr. Schatz wrote a letter to the editor of the *Journal*, Dr. Leland C. Hendershot. Dr. Schatz says the *Journal* refused to publish the letter and when he wrote a second letter it was returned to him unopened. Dr. Schatz thereupon wrote to the editor of the dental magazine, *Prevention*, and told the editor of the *Journal's* refusal to publish his letter. He asked that his comments be printed in *Prevention* so that the record would be set straight. This was done, together with some terse comments by Dr. Schatz on what he thought of American dentistry.

> . . . A stage has been now reached where the rejection of
> fluoridation will irreparably discredit the American Dental
> Association and the National Institute of Dental Research
> of the United States Health Service.
> Perhaps this is the explanation for the imposition of censor-
> ship on information concerning fluoridation . . .

A dentist friend of mine wrote the *Journal* on his stationery as a favor to me, requesting information about this accusation. Dr. Hendershot, editor of the *Journal*, readily admitted refusing to publish Dr. Schatz's letter because it would have allowed "him to use the *Journal* as a forum to promote his antifluoridation views." These, of course, are the views that Dr. Schatz feels he never announced in the first place.

Schatz and Martin have had many critics. There have been claims and counterclaims, articles and rebuttals. The language of these papers is clear and concise Academia, but sometimes not too damn polite. There are veiled accusations of incompetence, misquotation, misinterpretation, and worst of all, of publication before thinking, not always exactly between the lines. I have sampled some illustrative phrases from Schatz and Martin's letters and articles and from pieces by their detractors. With apologies for quoting out of context, here are some choice jibes:

> To the careful reader it will be apparent that the article by ———— has in no way strengthened their position.
>
> It is shocking you should condone must less support . . .
>
> We have always assumed that those who sign letters are responsible for what they wrote . . .
>
> Anyone who accepts ————'s work without recognizing its inadequacies, is obviously uninformed . . .
>
> . . . full of misconceptions, antiquated, and erroneous information . . .
>
> . . . proves the naïveté of those who have bothered to devote time to this . . .
>
> People should not make such statements unless they know what they're talking about . . .
>
> One can only conclude that ———— and ———— were inadequately prepared for the research which they undertook. People who conduct scientific studies have an obligation to familiarize both themselves and their readers with what is known about the problems on which they work . . .

Of course such comments usually accompany much more substantive arguments about the scientific issues. Nevertheless, personal attack is by no means absent in this controversy as these samples illustrate. If journalists fence with rapiers, scientists use scalpels; their weapons are a little sharper and less common, but the bodies get just as bloody.

Dr. Bernard Forscher, chairman of the Department of Biochemistry, School of Dentistry at the University of Kansas City, and Dr. Hamilton B. G. Robinson, Dean of the School of Dentistry at the University of Kansas City, are strong critics of Schatz. One of their main arguments has been that Schatz and Martin have not demonstrated their theories.

> . . . It is well within the accepted method of science to propose theories but one is also expected to conduct thorough and careful investigations to prove or disprove any proposed theory. Unfortunately, supporting data (relating to proteolysis-chelation) have been meager and, in our estimation, non-conclusive. Continuation of theorizing is no substitute for laboratory or clinical research.
>
> The "new" theory is an interesting example of applying the concepts of one science to the problems of another. However interesting Dr. Schatz's theory may be from a philosophical point of view we feel that the factual support and evidence presented do not warrant discarding the so-called acidogenic theory.

The reply of Drs. Schatz and Martin which appeared four months later in the same magazine provided some specific references to laboratory work that had been accomplished and supported their theories. Yet Forscher and Robinson are asking for some overpowering demonstration of his ideas; the burden of proof is on the innovator.

A summary of Schatz and Martin's work shows that they

received funded support from the U.S. Public Health Service and the New York Academy of Dentistry between 1954 and 1957 to investigate proteolysis-chelation. I asked Dr. Schatz about his problems of research funding and he wrote me:

> . . . I had no difficulty in getting the first grants because I did not at that time oppose the acid theory or those who supported it. When I bucked them, they told me to stop or they would take my grant support away. Just like that! I told them I was not a prostitute and was not for sale, that I damn well would go (in the direction my results took me). That was in 1956. Since then I have had no grant support. What I've done . . . has come out of my own pocket . . . There is no possibility that I know of to get funds from any source in the United States for work on proteolysis-chelation. Any agency to which I might apply would enquire of the American Dental Association or the National Institute of Dental Research if I were a reputable researcher or if my proposal had merit and the answer would be a flat *no*.
>
> Dr. ——— got turned down three times . . . I advised him that since he was a young guy just starting out in the research racket that he should not get into this fight. I could afford it; he could not and although I wanted and desperately needed independent confirmation, I advised him for his own sake to stay the hell out because they would "kill" him professionally if he stuck his neck out on a hot problem such as this.

In 1956 a questionnaire was mailed to consultant experts familiar with bacterial proteolysis and chelation in non-dental fields. The object of this inquiry was to elicit opinions about whether Schatz and Martin were off on the wrong track (their research was just starting then) or whether their non-dental colleagues found merit in their ideas. Forty authorities answered. Obviously scientific truth is not determined by a show of hands; this exercise was merely to determine whether the fundamentals underlying his concept were based on sound (contemporary) scientific logic. The great majority of the consultants expressed a dissatisfaction with the acid theory, most answered that proteolysis-chelation seemed a more suitable theory, and the non-dental experts agreed that Schatz and Martin's basic concepts are valid. In view of this endorsement, why has there not been more funding?

Some other new ideas are showing up in this field of dental research. If proteolysis-chelation eventually proves to be incorrect, perhaps one of these other new innovations will hold the key. Some researchers are working with an emotional stress theory; the higher the tension of the subject, the more likely he is to have cavities. Other workers are experimenting with mechanical stress and are trying to relate caries formation to forces developed in a tooth when chewing. These concepts illustrate how "inter-disciplinary" this field has become—now caries involves not only dental mechanics and "classic" acid research, but microbiologists, soil chemists, thermodynamists, mechanical engineers, molecular physicists, chemists, and psychologists. Perhaps the eventual solution to caries will tax the skill of all of these specialists; perhaps when we find the answer to caries we will gain some insight into the mechanics of the sociology of science.

# (11

# FUNDSVILLE

The research required to validate or disprove new ideas cannot be accomplished without money and generally, the more
controversial the work, the more difficult it is to obtain support. Without some source of funds, new ideas remain only
interesting topics of conversation. In the process of collect-
ing material for the chapters of this book, in interviewing
the principals, their protagonists, their colleagues and anti-
colleagues, I found that funding was a subject with its own
special taboos; we could talk frankly and openly about incompetence on the other guy's part, complete with names,
dates, and documentation, but when we came to funding,
that hard-core primordial green stuff from which all research
springs, the discussion would often go "off-the-record." One

scientist gave me complete details on the policies and politics of his funding picture and I originally included this story in one of these chapters. After he reviewed the original manuscript, he wrote me with some obvious doubts in mind. About a month later a close colleague of his called me and said essentially: "Look, old Joe is a hell of a good guy. What you've said about his funding problems and what he thinks of those guys in Washington is true enough. But if that ever gets into print, he'll never get another nickel." So I deleted it. I won't be accused of impeding science.

This episode and others like it convinced me that part of the conflict of ideas stems from the way in which science projects derive their funds in our society.

The spectrum of scientific activity can be divided into "little science" and "big science" at least in the administrative and fiscal domain. "Big science" involves those massive government facilities that require large initial expenditures and operational costs. These facilities are designed to probe specific scientific areas and generally require approval by Congress.

The National Radio Astronomy Observatory at Green Bank, the electron accelerator at Stanford University, the Ionospheric Observatory in Puerto Rico are all examples of this category of spending. Typically these facilities are manned by scientists recruited from various universities who in one way or another derive their salaries from the public tax dollar. Big science can be very big indeed; the *Apollo* program will cost a total of at least 20 billion dollars to put a man on the moon. *Apollo* also illustrates another feature of "big science." National political objectives override the interests of pure introverted science, which is, perhaps, as it should be since the government is paying the bill.

"Little science" refers to that portion of our scientific

activity supervised by single individuals and their immediate staffs in small laboratories, working on projects involving expenditures of less than ½ million dollars or so. This amount goes mostly for the salaries of the researchers. Much of our most important new scientific work is being accomplished in this way today.

Independent scientists engaged in "little science" are the small businessmen of the innovation industry. They can derive funds for their projects in several ways. First, they can solicit funds from sponsoring individuals or corporations. In this arrangement, the sponsor usually takes an option on the possible proprietary inventions that are expected from the research. This is private capital at work.

Some scientists work directly for industry. Here the long-range goals of the corporation set the objectives for the research. The scientists in their company laboratories work ultimately toward the profit goal. There are some corporations, however, which allow their researchers to tackle any project that interests them on the theory that: (1) it creates a good corporate image; (2) maybe something of value will come out of it, and (3) it's deductible anyway.

This leaves the scientists who work in the laboratories of universities or nonprofit institutes. In some cases the institution pays for the work of its scientists, relying on endowments or other sources of funds, but more often the work is paid for by the government. The scientists working in these laboratories conceive and outline a project, interest a government agency in the work, and eventually receive a contract to perform the research. But a lot of marketing, public relations, and old-fashioned politicking goes on between the conception of a line of research and the contract.

The grant and contract system for "little science" seems to be working. There are approximately 100,000 scientists engaged in full-time "little science" projects at the present time. The average cost for each man has been estimated as $20,000 per year. This represents a two billion dollar annual investment in basic research. Sixty percent of this money comes from the government. The other 40% is funded by industry, the universities themselves and other nonprofit institutions.

In the deep past, before the term "little science" had meaning, research into basic science was supported almost entirely by private funds. In that era the university professor would typically teach and work in his university laboratory with graduate students and assistants, following the lines of inquiry which he found rewarding. The picture is not entirely idyllic; often equipment was inadequate, funds were limited and schedules overly demanding. Nevertheless, some scientists, taking stock of themselves today, worry that easy funding has caused scientific ingenuity to suffer at the altar of governmental abundance. It may be easier and faster to devise sloppy, complex, expensive experiments than to sharpen the intellect in the determination of a simple, but crucial test.

But the ready abundance is a fact of scientific life; for good or evil, it is something that must be lived with. And as in all such exigencies of our modern world, knowledge of only a few of the basic rules pertaining to the techniques of grant-getting can mark the difference between academic affluence and poverty.

With apologies to Parkinson, I have attempted to set down these principles and present here a guide to grants, a freeway to funding, so to speak. These rules have been gleaned from the experiences of the heroes of this book, and their enemies. I learned from the failures of some and the successes of others. Here is life in the science factory.

To insure the highest probability of obtaining a grant, one must first carefully study the trend of the scientific *mode de jour*. There are fashions in science as surely as in women's bathing suits. Today it's biochemistry; the cell's the thing. This is our new frontier. Last decade the glamour discipline was nuclear physics. A research subject which is in vogue marks the proposer as one of the "in" crowd. I certainly recommend such a choice to a novice or even an intermediate fund seeker.

To find the trend I would suggest a careful continuing survey of symposia papers, charting the statistical distribution of the subject matter among disciplines. Any abrupt shift in emphasis shoud be carefully scrutinized.

One can acquire a knack for identifying the trends *before* they actually happen. When this skill is well developed, the researcher can submit a proposal slightly in advance of the coming wave of interest. In this way he is marked as farsighted. While funding may be more difficult to obtain initially, his reputation will advance a few notches, so that the payoff will be enjoyed in later years. There is a warning here though—if one misses this trend prediction, he will not be called farsighted, he will be Bohemian, working on the fringes, not doing really interesting and important work—odd, or worse, crank.

Having made the choice of subject matter, the next problem is one of agency. Government agencies which provide funds for research may be classed as "pure" or mission directed. The National Science Foundation is pure; i.e., it can fund general-purpose basic research. Mission-directed agencies, such as the Atomic Energy Commission and the National Aeronautics and Space Administration are interested in furthering that research connected directly with their charter, although they sometimes also buy proposals that appear to the layman to be rather general purpose. I have no first-hand knowledge of how this is managed, but I suppose that a few *proper* words, in the jargon of the agency, will help. Suppose a geologist wants to do research in sedimentary rocks of the Amazon Valley. A proposal to NASA should certainly contain phrases like: "suspected similarity to the mantles of extraterrestrial bodies" or "selenology" or "represents dynamic process of planetary formation which may provide insight into," etc. If this same proposal were directed to the Atomic Energy Commission it should probably include these phrases: "analysis of the natural products of radioactive decay," or "substrata investigations into primordial cosmic ray intensity." I do not offer these as complete examples, but they are illustrative of the technique. The industrious student will find it instructive to list the mission-oriented funding agencies and, using his own ingenuity, index key jargon for each. Remember, the right words will help your project: conversely, almost nothing infuriates a funding agency more than being addressed in the language of another discipline. Using the right words is almost like a mark of respect.

This leads to the next point, humility. Don't be a know-it-all scientist in your proposal. Funding agencies seem to go for a questioning attitude. Even if you're dead sure you're on the right track don't say it. A much better technique would be to question your original approach even if results were positive. Ask for a chance to find out what you did wrong before, particularly if your work is in conflict with the majority opinion.

Closely allied with humility is humor—or rather lack of it. Don't be funny about your work, even in private conversations. Somehow, if it's funny, it's unscientific. Look at McConnell and the *Worm Runner's Digest*.

Then there is the delicate matter of the punch line—somehow, no matter how good a scientist you are, no matter what your reputation, independent of your humility and lack of humor, somehow you have to say, "I need $X$ dollars." There are some very delicate rules to follow here obviously, but I think the most important is this: estimate your costs carefully. Include everything, new test tubes, trips to symposia, publication costs, secretarial fees, consultants. Be accurate. When you have arrived at a figure, double it and then submit it. Too low a figure is always cause for suspicion—this work might not be worthy of the agency. I knew a scientist who submitted, in his first proposal, an estimate of $15,000 for one year's work. He thought this modest price couldn't miss. The agency turned him down. Their note said that *"programs of this scope are generally financed by university departments."* Since the proposed project wasn't, something was apparently fishy, so no dice. The next year he rewrote the proposal, covering essentially the same work, but asked for $30,000. He got the grant. Although there may have been other factors involved, I believe, as does he, that the price change was the new essential ingredient.

Finding out who within the agency is responsible for your area of interest is not always easy. Some, perhaps most, government agencies have very complex organizational structures, with overlapping responsibilities. Yet it is important that initial contact with the agency be made at precisely the proper organizational level. A first contact at too high a level and the real decision-makers will become incensed that they were bypassed when the head of the agency finally asks their opinion; too low and the potential proposal will bounce from office to office being appended with nonessential recommendations and commentary. When your proposal finally hits the right level, it may be already obsolete. More insidiously, it may start its real review with a negative bias simply because it was endorsed by a civil servant out of favor with the administration.

Incidentally, every agency has a grant application form. You will have to fill out this form eventually, but don't be fooled. Your own personal contacts are necessary before submitting it. Application for the funds, sent in cold, will invariably get the response: "Who in the hell does that guy think he is?" The smart researcher will have built his bridges before the fateful mailing. Tactics here include sending a manuscript of yours to the right man in the agency, asking for his comments before you submit it for publication. Letters to the editor of scientific journals can be helpful occasionally, but perhaps most helpful is the intermediate or direct presubmittal contact. In the scientific community there is a very efficient subsurface system of keeping track of who's where. Through publications, personal contact, and word of mouth the positions and interests of the community's elite are generally widely known, in fact followed in the same sense that the lay public follows the career of Sandy Koufax. It is usually possible and certainly recommended that any scientist seeking a grant make some discreet inquiries first about who's in charge in Washington, and the political climate in the authorizing agency.

Then, either in person, or through an intermediary, become known around the agency. This approach can be carried to extremes. Let me cite an example (a real case) of two behavioral scientists who have a plan to submit publications and letters, even symposia papers, to various editors over the signature of a fictitious scientist. The papers would be copied from old texts, but rewritten to bring the footnotes, language and jargon up to date. Since these papers are generally unread they are confident they would avoid detection. Gradually they would build up the reputation of their fictitious scientist to the point where their now-known scientist would apply for a grant. You can take the scenario anywhere you want from this point: inglorious exposure by a vindictive agency administration; Brazil and native girls for the two behavioral scientists; perhaps final admission that the whole hoax was an experiment itself in the sociology of science.

In summary then, remember:

(1) a good reputation gets the grants.
(2) follow the *mode de jour*.
(3) select your jargon to fit the agency.
(4) don't be a know-it-all.
(5) be modest and self-questioning.
(6) be as unfunny as possible.
(7) ask for plenty.
(8) go in at the right organizational level.

You can't hardly lose.

I could go on and describe some other aspects of the grant process such as form filling—the grant form of the National Institute of Health, for example, is only a single page. The 100 page NIH grant manual is required reading—but I suspect the serious student would benefit most by some actual field trials.

Such are the exigencies of government funding of "little science." Control of a major portion of our basic research by mission directed agencies raises the specter of government interference in an essentially artistic and creative process. "How can any man," the argument goes, "foresee the ulti-mate result of basic scientific inquiry? Who could have fore-seen that theoretical computations of Einstein would lead eventually to Hiroshima? Who could have guaranteed they would not?" The consensus of scientists, at least based on a report of the National Academy of Sciences, indicates that the direction of basic research should be decentralized. There is no better judge in determining what work a scientist should pursue, they imply, than the scientist himself, since the eventual utility of his discoveries is unknown. He should, they say, work on what interests him for that is where his contribution can be made.

As a taxpayer, I object, and since the money is largely mine, I have a right to object. The criterion for work undertaken with public funds should be not that which interests the *scientist*, but that which is to the benefit of the *people*. In this I am willing to let the scientist and his peers be the judge. Can we not add one question to the bottom of each grant application form? I would add: How will this work help man? I am even willing to trust to a jury of scientists to judge the answer. I will freely admit that the answer to the question will often be wrong. There will be proposed work which will appear beneficial but which will be evil in application. There will be good work undone because the good remains unknown before the research. But certainly *some* judgment is better than none. Public funding demands public good. You and I choose our actions based on concepts of morality—why shouldn't science?

Where would we be without government support of "little science?" Where are we going with it?

"Big science" is part of today's national politics. I need cite only one example to make this point. A 200 billion electron volt proton accelerator is being considered by the government. Suddenly this tool is more than a scientific device; in the age of "big science" it's big politics. The project will cost $280,000,000 if original estimates are met. The laboratory will employ 2000 people. The operating costs of the accelerator will be $60,000,000 per year. It will be the most costly single scientific instrument ever built, including instruments developed for the space program. While politicians may not understand the workings of the accelerator they can certainly visualize its pork barrel aspects.

Why do we want to build it? For the sake of science and international politics. The higher the energy of such a tool, the more we expect to find out about the elemental construction of matter. This is a good scientific justification. On the political side, the Russians will complete a 70 billion electron volt accelerator in 1966. It will be the world's most powerful unit, until the U.S. has finished this 200 BEV job.

The Atomic Energy Commission asked the Lawrence Radiation Laboratory of the University of California at Berkeley to design the accelerator. When it came to determining where this accelerator would be built, the AEC asked for proposals from the states. As of July 1965, some ninety-three proposals had been received from forty-three states. Most states saw the new constituents, roads, schools, washeterias, and general affluence resulting from the project and offered to pitch in money of their own to entice the government to their proposed site. Governor Roger D. Branigin of Indiana called the project, "the scientific prize of the century." Representative Craig Hosmer (R., Long Beach) has criticized the administration for its indecision in selecting a site. Hosmer's district did not offer a proposal.

The AEC has called on the National Academy of Sciences to help make the decision. The NAS will judge, nonpolitically, on the advantages of each proposal, but the government must ultimately make the choice.

But who is to run the accelerator? In January 1965 a group of thirty-four presidents met in "virtual secrecy" to discuss the administration of the facility. Of this meeting D. S. Greenberg reports in *Science:*

> . . . The motive for establishing the (inter-university) organization was a laudatory one—to dampen regional strife by getting universities across the nation to cooperate in the administration and use of the costly machines of science. It is perhaps unfortunate, though, that (the meeting of university presidents) was organized without any notice or discussion . . . Traditionally that's the way of doing business at the summit of the scientific community, but it's not the way to inspire public or congressional confidence, especially when the principal business of the association is expected of the administration of taxpayer supported science.

This group, Universities Research Association, Inc., has offered their services to the government to run the facility. They will probably get the job since their number includes almost all of the prestigious schools involved in high energy physics research. Who can compete with such a group? Yet there may be dissention within their ranks. *Science* magazine wonders about this also:

> . . . Whether URAI can suppress the combative inclinations of the high-energy physicists remains to be seen. Partly as the result of a process of professional selection, they are an ingenious, energetic bunch, and they are stirred to battle by the realization that, in addition to highly charged particles, the big machine also turns out Nobel prizes and other glory. "Time on the machine" is the issue underlying much of the strife. Who gets time, when there isn't enough for all the ambitious applicants, is never going to be a courteously settled question, no matter what the organization.

On an even bigger scale, achievements in the sciences offer to the nations of the world a medium by which they may exert political power. Political power is that property of international leadership which enables a nation to influence the policy of other nations to its ends. Just as war has been recognized as an instrument of politics, so now must science. I propose that enhancement of our political situation is an important objective which should be, and to a degree has been, seriously considered in planning our current big-science projects.

It may not be necessary today, in this world of status quo, to wage war to convince an enemy nation that you can wage war and win or at least break even. This is the hope of our hydrogen standoff. In this situation any new innovation by the enemy must be weighed carefully in the balance of power. In a precisely matched international situation it is the demonstration of new principles or technologies that can swing leadership from one side to the other.

This edge does not have to be military. Our political position would be considerably enhanced through discoveries of basic research and the developments which follow. If we were to discover the key to heredity control for example, we would have demonstrated to the cold war world our advanced understanding of the material world (good for a few brownie points at least) and perhaps forced our enemies to reconsider our power and importance. This is sort of a Tom Sawyer game but our own past achievements and the evenly distributed destructive power in the world has forced us here.

We have been concerned with the economic problems associated with disarmament or reduction in the rate of production of armaments. Big science has an important interface here; Professor Fred Neal puts the problem this way:

> . . . It is easy for a college professor, for example, to advocate disarmament. But it is not at all easy for one whose day-to-day livelihood comes from making armaments, even

if he sees, in the abstract, the advisability of it. Before there can be a meaningful breakthrough toward even arms control, there must be a federal agency with the authority and the means to guarantee that no worker, no businessman, and even no investor suffer as a result of armament agreements.

Spending money in the science industry and its derivatives can provide an acceptable alternative to armament expenditures, while meeting the politically oriented goals of the nation. Thus, science can supplant war, not only as a means of exerting political power but as an economic stimulant to the nation.

Clearly, our science program provides a way to spend a significant portion of the national budget in those areas of the country which need such economic assistance. This is consistent with President Johnson's approach to the Great Society. To some, the concept of awarding contracts on the basis of economic need rather than technical competence, is repugnant. The idea of providing contracts to depressed areas can be made consistent with awarding contracts on the basis of competence by simply requiring that certain aspects of planning, design, or fabrication be accomplished at the desired geographic sites. This implies that the government would have to provide facilities in the desired areas so that the winning agencies could perform their work where the government finds it most advantageous to spend money. Of course, this has happened and is happening today.

Planned scientific expenditures can also be used to develop scientific and technological talents, an important national resource. By the careful selection of goals for our programs, our national planners can assure the training, employment, and development of large segments of our innovators. In our economy innovation must continue. It is only through innovation that we can cope with problems that have resulted from our own advanced technologies, such as air pollution, power generation in the face of decreasing natural resources, automation, and collection and dissemination of technical information. We can develop the scientific technological competence needed to solve these problems by proper shaping of our immediate goals.

We can also use our work in science and technology as a kind of foreign aid, enticing uncommitted nations to cooperate with us. For example, if we were to order a space guidance system from Brazil, we would not only help that country develop its technology and thereby its economic stature, but we would provide it with a degree of self-assurance which is often lacking with the outright foreign aid gifts. Imagine the international effect of flying a payload built by scientists from India on a U.S. vehicle. The model for such international cooperation has already been set on a small scale in the American flights of British and Canadian payloads on the Delta space vehicle. Such cooperative efforts could be vastly expanded in order to draw into our political orbit nations which wish to participate with us in the exploration of space.

These invitations for international cooperation are stimulants of the highest order. Introducing dollars into foreign economies in this way would not only provide immediate dollar value, but would, in turn, provide occupations for those employed in the newly founded innovation businesses, impetus for added education, technological advancement; all of this without the loss of self-respect by the receiving nation. Imagine the prestige which we could lend to uncommitted nations if we invited them to provide experiments which would be among the first to land men on the moon. Would this not tend to make them our allies?

So it seems that science, be it big or little, is almost inseparable from politics and government. The two have formed in today's world an implicit alliance which may prove to be stronger and more enduring than the marriage of religion and government which is only now ending. The United States is not unique among nations in creating this new partnership; almost all nations are investing heavily in research and development; almost all nations are experimenting with various centralization and authorization schemes for the control of politically inspired research. Research expenditures have accounted for a rapidly increasing proportion of the gross national product of many countries including the United States, Great Britain, France, Japan, the Netherlands, Canada, Iceland, India, and probably Russia and China. We are, of course, less certain of the statistics of the expenditures of the Communist nations, but this trend is probably occurring there also, judging from public statements made by their scientific and political leaders. Today research and scientific innovation may be equated not only with progress, but survival.

To a degree, administration of scientific research is simpler in Communist societies. All enterprises including projects of scientific research and technological development, are financed, controlled and managed by the government. There is no quibbling about who should decide the goals to be followed; clearly, it is the state. The goals relate not to the glory of science, or science for the sake of science, or morality, but to the preplanned objectives of the country and its citizens as interpreted by its political leaders. One need only look at Russia's efforts in space to understand that it is the government alone that decides what shall be undertaken in big science, even if the consumer must wait, a little cold and a little uncomfortable, for his slice of the national resources and brain power. Not only is Russia hop-

ing for a direct military pay-off from its research investment, it sees that innovation and discovery can be the key
to economic enlargement.

Little science in the Soviet Union is accomplished through
a series of academies, organized along the lines of the different scientific disciplines. These organizations are essentially centralized planning agencies which effectively control a number of separate and semi-autonomous institutes.
Each institute is headed by a director who is responsible
for accomplishing the assigned research program and the
maintenance of the institute itself. He is appointed by the
head of the Academy for, typically, a renewable three-year
term. He has a deputy vice-director immediately under him,
whose title is usually appended with "for research." Reporting to the vice-director are a number of department
heads who execute the program of the institute in its laboratories. There is a well-developed hierarchy here too. In
each institute there is a Scientific Council which is responsible for monitoring the research plan of the institute and
reviewing the progress of its individual studies. It is this
body which is expected to rule on all issues involving "scientific problems." It serves as an executive committee and a
jury of peers. It would be interesting to know how they
handle their ideas in conflict. What happens there when a
young research assistant stands up before the group and
says, "I think . . ." and the learned Council disagrees?

China also is pursuing scientific goals. There the central
scientific planning agency is the Science and Technology
Commission. Here is their view of the role of research and
development:

> First, scientific and technological work should be made to
> serve the general interests of socialist construction, in-
> cluding economic and national-defense construction . . .

> Whether our scientific and technological work is able to coordinate with and promote our economic and national defense construction will be the principal yardstick in measuring the success of our scientific and technological work . . .

Chinese research has already paid off by giving them the atomic bomb; there is reason to believe that this research is continuing toward the hydrogen bomb, effective delivery systems and other mechanisms of military power. Its leaders picture China catching up with the United States in industrial production, agricultural production, and in science and technology. If they can do it, an aggressive China, and a massive army of perhaps 50,000,000 soldiers, would represent a tremendous danger to the world.

There is also some evidence that the value of broader based "little science" has been realized in China. Publications over the past few years have indicated that intensified basic research as well as technological development has been established as a national goal. In 1956 a twelve year scientific program was announced which included: "the prevention and eradication of a number of diseases most detrimental to the people's health, and (solution to) important problems of basic theory in the natural sciences." Of course, these projects received lower priority than those technological developments that would directly enhance the nation's economy or military force. While some revisions of this plan have occurred over the years, little science is still part of China's science planning.

Here then is the dilemma: national manipulation and direction of research and development has become a tool of international politics. The governments with centralized planning can direct their internal efforts along lines that appear to enhance over-all national goals. In free societies such centralized planning is distasteful. Yet in "big science" the very magnitude of the expenditures involved demand close legislative and budget scrutiny. This gives the governments control over the projects, which almost automatically makes them subject to internal political pressures. The research scientists engaged in "little science" say, "Let us work on projects of our choice. We will discover unknown things which will make our country great. Trust us." Yet, in our country, there seem to be few efficient organizational mechanisms available for disseminating funds without strings attached.

Science and government have wed. World leadership, perhaps survival, depends on these partners working out their differences. The children of this marriage, the innovations which will make tomorrow, might be good, pleasant and wholesome, a source of enjoyment and satisfaction to their parents in their old age. But their progeny can also be evil, selfish and patricidal. It is a behavioral problem of the gravest importance.

(12

# THE
# NATURE
# OF THE
# BEAST

So these are some of the men whose ideas have met controversy: Velikovsky, with his concept of catastrophe, which
runs counter to the prevalent image of the constant world,
slowly changing in response to demands of natural selection, an image formed after the wave of evolutionism of the
nineteenth century; Rhine and Loehr, who argue for the acceptance of forces which cannot today be measured, forces
called supernatural, the anathema of quantified science since
the emergence of the scientific method after the Renais-
sance; McConnell, with his learning experiments, which
suggest a new mechanism of memory, and, in asexual reproduction at least, that learned behavior can be inherited;
Leary, who has combined pharmacology with pure ex-

perience; Drake, a man present at the birth of a new discipline, exobiology; Sisler, whose work suggests that life on
earth may not have come from classic, evolutionary spontaneous generation, but from outer space, either as viable
organisms or as protolife molecules; Nagy, with his probing
experiments that apparently show the existence of life elsewhere, but leave unanswered the question of its origin;
Ettinger, who has married some scientific concepts to logic,
and argued these to the point where immortality can be
offered to the common man; and Schatz, a man devoted to
proving that the preconceptions and hypotheses of an entire community may be incorrect, that caries may be caused
by mechanisms other than acid attack.

Some of these men are more "scientific" than others;
some of their ideas are more "believable" and "appealing"
than others. But what makes certain of them appear more
"scientific" or "believable" or "appealing"? Is it not that they
fit in with our preconceived ideas of nature?

There have been several attempts to probe and understand the mechanisms of scientific progress from an historical point of view. Perhaps the most outstanding of these
is the brilliant work by Thomas Kuhn in his *The Structure
of Scientific Revolutions*. Professor Kuhn probed the history
of science from a philosophical vantage and formed the
conclusion that scientific progress is not an orderly evolution, not a simple cumulative progression of ideas, but
rather a series of crises, discontinuities in ideas and techniques, mutations, which in the aggregate form progress.
The conflicts we have just examined represent, perhaps,
some crises in progress.

Science normally forces nature into neat conceptual
boxes. The boxes contain certain facts, theories, and methods that are appropriate to the discipline. They form a way

of looking at a set of phenomena which has been found to produce predictable and acceptable results. The information in the box is what is taught to scientists in training; it is the information from which textbooks are constructed; it is a constrained view of one particular aspect of the world which must be believed. This belief is the ticket of admission as a scientist. This material, this set of ground rules, Dr. Kuhn calls a paradigm.

Once a paradigm is stated and accepted, certain legitimate problems are opened to scientific investigation. It is the business of normal science to probe these open questions, to determine significant facts which add to the precision of the paradigm, to test the paradigm in a variety of new situations, to resolve ambiguities in the original articulation of the rules of the game. In other words, normal science, which is the major occupation of scientists, is not directed toward novelty; it is directed toward the refinement of a previously stated position.

Paradigms, nature images, provide continuity to science. A new scientist can take up where others have left off. The rules form a road map, a plan of attack, a device by which diverse specialists can work toward a common end. In this common attack, results are cumulative, leading to more precise articulation of the paradigm.

Since some of the old ideas which science once held as inviolable have been replaced and buried; it is clear that old paradigms sometimes die. For example, phrenology, phlogiston, caloric, are all dead ideas, replaced by more viable concepts of nature. As the work of normal science progresses, anomalies are sometimes uncovered. The old ideas don't fit the new data; the paradigm fails in prediction; fact and theory no longer match. These failures do not lead immediately to the formation of new conceptual boxes because to flatly reject the old concept with no alternative is unacceptable. Sometimes the anomalous data are shelved in hopes that continued work within the paradigm ground rules will resolve the discrepancy. But if continued work blurs rather than sharpens the nature image, a crisis is likely. A crisis comes, according to Kuhn, when that which was believed previously is no longer a sound foundation for continued research. Such a conclusion has important consequences. The firmament is gone; that which was taught by revered instructors is false; the heroes are wrong. The stimulus no longer brings reward; it brings frustration. The psychological analogy is clear. In laboratory experiments similar situations are devised to induce clinical frustration. The crisis ends only with the statement of a new paradigm.

In the absence of a working paradigm, all facts have almost equal weight since there is no map by which the important may be separated from the trivial. Dr. Kuhn has noted that in a preparadigm phase, innovators may write books that appeal to wider audiences than the papers that are produced as a part of normal science. The books are necessary since they, in effect, start at the beginning and try to pick up the pieces of the broken theory. But a new theory is not likely to be accepted unless a crisis clearly exists. The retooling is simply too difficult.

There have been many cases when new paradigms have been proposed before a crisis was evident. These are usually rejected since the business of science is being conducted well enough on the old principles. When a new concept is needed because of failure of the old, it is likely that competing ideas will be stated and the community will choose sides. Some scientists will never accept any alternative to their "home base" theory, those ideas which served so well in the past. They wait for vindication of their sacred principles and sometimes die with their beliefs. A new paradigm must resolve the outstanding crisis, and preserve much of the body of previous accomplishment. There is no appeal, no judge higher than the community itself. When the debates between contending ideas have passed and scientists have accepted the new working hypothesis, history is rewritten, and the narrow confines of the new conceptual box are presented as "truth" to the new scientists in training. Normal science resumes and the probing of the new idea, the exploration of its limits, begins again.

Permitting my own imperfect retelling, this is Dr. Kuhn's own paradigm defining the working of science. While he has based these observations on extensive study of the history of science, we can immediately detect many of these patterns running through the contemporary narratives that formed the previous chapters. We have seen cases of paradigms being offered before crises exist; precrises examples of anomalous "normal" science experiments; preparadigm fact gathering; and appeal to authority other than the community itself.

Dr. Schatz, for example, has tried to convince dentistry, which has not yet recognized a crisis, that its acidogenic tradition may be wrong. Velikovsky, with his brilliant books that retell creation in terms of catastrophe, is picking up the pieces of a crisis before the community is ready to declare that any picking up is necessary.

The prayer work of Loehr and Rhine's ESP investigations are probing areas in which no paradigm exists; theirs is the preparadigm experience. They have started with fact gathering, and in each retelling of their story, they start again with basic observations. There is as yet no device for predicting accurately, no foundation on which to build other than repetitions of the experiments which illustrate their findings.

McConnell, Drake, Sisler, and Nagy are working within normal science, but they are poking into the corners of the neat boxes of their disciplines, coaxing their paradigms to give answers where none have existed before. In their poking, McConnell, Sisler, and Nagy have found discrepancies in their paradigms, for which there is no ready answer; Drake is godfather to a new discipline.

Loehr, in his work with prayer, Leary with his experimental LSD activity, and Ettinger with his freeze-the-body plan would seem to be working outside of science, in a direct interplay with the lay public, using their interpretations of science. It is important to them to appeal to the public rather than the scientific community for endorsement. Thus Dr. Kuhn's generalizations drawn from history seem to hold, at least superficially, for these contemporary ideas.

An idea which bucks a paradigm usually runs into trouble. "Trouble" in this sense means that the innovator may be denied means of communication and research open to normal science. Inability to publish in technical media, rejection of papers offered to symposia, restricted or nonexistent funding, rejection by innuendo through the use of cautionary labels when papers are presented or printed, article for article and editorial for editorial rebuttal: all of these are techniques of denial. If the trouble is deep enough, the repression may become organized.

How do the innovators react to these denials? The spectrum of responses to these inhibitions include publishing one's own journals and organizing one's own symposia, appealing to the public at large, and deriving funding through private institutions, perhaps even forming these institutions to support the new concept. In no case here was an appeal made to church or government. Thus the establishment is fought largely on its own grounds, using its rules. The only exception, in some cases, is the appeal to the public which seems to be singularly ineffective, in promoting the acceptance of new ideas by the scientific community.

As for the innovators themselves, there seems to be a certain vitality, a sense of excitement, of complete involvement about them. Time was precious but they always found time to explain again, and often in this explanation, the force of their personalities outweighed, or at least overpowered, the force of their arguments. The men came through as men who believed in what they were saying and would believe it through opposition and inquisition. Some were as parochial as their antagonists, permitting no criticism, accepting no compromise. It struck me that many of these men enjoyed their role as avant-garde innovators; in some this role was flavored with a little martyr complex. Some of the innovators wrote outside of their fields. This gave them the advantage of "selective ignorance" of the paradigms they were attacking, but aroused distrust. Sometimes their jargon didn't match the discipline, which was even worse. Remarkably, in most cases, the proposing of a novel idea did not seem to impede the careers of the innovators. Perhaps this was because the innovators could carry on other normal science functions while their controversy was continuing in adjacent fields. The innovators themselves seemed to realize the necessity for convincing the community and were willing to work at that task. Success means recognition. Success means priority. Success means, Ettinger aside, immortality.

The innovators were a most impressive group. Scientists who have not broken with convention or pushed the limits of normal science may also be impressive. Charlatans, adept at gab, may be the most impressive of the lot. I found no formula for distinguishing the potential contributor from the pretentious crackpot. At best formulas which have been proposed, such as the one mentioned in the first chapter, can distinguish those who are working outside the bounds of normal science. This is no test for nonparadigm innovation.

Before an idea is accepted into the body of "science" its practitioners are generally marked as "odd." For example, I was discussing this book with one of the innovators I have described. When I told him that I intended to include the stories of several other embattled ideas, he said, "I'm not sure I want to appear in a book with a bunch of kooks. My ideas are sound, but how do I know about them?"

Another scientist, in recommending a possible subject for this book, wrote me, "Just one word of warning. Though ———'s credentials are excellent, and though he is clearly a bright, literate, and perceptive person, he may also be a crank. If you do write him, I should try to establish some sort of escape hatch through which you could retreat if you do not like what you hear."

So the dilemma is this: a new idea must be carefully scrutinized before it can be accepted. It generally will not be accepted if there is no demonstrated need for it. Yet it may be right. Its prophets may be inhibited in expressing their views and have difficulty in deriving funds to perform experiments that might validate their views. Furthermore, there is no simple test that can distinguish the valid from the vacuous. Is there an answer? Let us take the two key issues in turn: publication and funding.

Technical journals are vital to science and technology because these publications now serve as one of the most important means of disseminating information throughout a discipline and across disciplines. Aside from the articles themselves, almost every journal contains a news section where significant events in sister fields are brought to the attention of its readers. Similarly, it is important for a scientist to publish in these journals for two reasons: first, it communicates discovery to other workers in the field, and second, it provides an acceptable means of advertising, an important consideration in career planning. Personal recognition is very important to the advancement of a scientist, perhaps as important as it is to the career of a movie star. In science as in other enterprises, known names are considered first for new job opportunities. An aspiring movie star can advertise in *Variety;* the published writings of a scientist can serve the same purpose. They mark him personally as a contributor. In the scientific and technical community, then, there are valid reasons for the publication of technical journals, and valid reasons to read and write for them.

Even with normal science articles, the road to publication in the big name journals can be a little rocky. With priority at stake, it is sometimes urgent to publish as soon as words and concept can be committed to paper. To satisfy this need, several magazines such as *Physical Review Letters* specialize in fast scientific publication. The drive to get into print apparently causes some authors to be a little sloppy and others to resort to a little refined in-fighting. An editor for this magazine recently said:

> . . . We never cease to be amazed that so many authors who consider their work to be highly significant and urgent don't take the time to make a careful last minute check for typographical errors, omissions, possible ambiguities, unclear remarks, and flaws in figures . . . We do not take kindly

to attempts to pressure us into accepting Letters by misrepresentation, gamesmanship, and jungle tactics, which we have experienced to some (fortunately small) extent.

For some reason these professional journals do not like to be scooped. Not only is there apparent rivalry among magazines serving the same discipline, but the journals seem to agree that prior publication in a popular medium should be avoided at all costs. This attitude was clearly stated in another remarkably frank editorial in *Physical Review Letters:*

> . . . As a matter of courtesy to fellow physicists, it is customary for authors to see to it that releases to the public do not occur before the article appears in the scientific journal. Scientific discoveries are not the proper subject for newspaper scoops, and all media of mass communication should have equal opportunity for simultaneous access to the information. In the future we may reject papers whose main content has been published previously in the daily press.

Notice the pressure: ". . . we may reject papers whose main content has been published previously in the daily press." I wonder what would happen if a physicist chose to publish in a weekly? Or in *Time*? How about *Playboy*?

Which brings us to a tale about interjournal rivalry. Almost every technical journal has a scientific jury, a panel of referees that judge the merit of articles prior to their acceptance by the publisher. Sometimes these juries champion alternate sides of a controversy and the magazines then can take a very competitive and biased position. This has happened several times and in the extreme has resulted in the failure of one or the other periodicals. I had recounted one example of this kind of publication rivalry in one of these chapters but, for reasons that will become apparent, I have chosen to present it here incognito, as a fantasy.

Once there were two scientific journals of highest competence; let us call them *Journal of the Applied Insight* and *Proceedings of the Perception Institute*. They both covered articles of general scientific interest and co-existed happily. Then one day a Young Scientist submitted an article about his new concept to the *Journal*. One of the referees for the *Journal* happened to be Professor M who had publicly criticized the new concept. Result: the article was rejected. When I asked Young Scientist why he thought this had happened he shrugged his shoulders and said philosophically, "Editor's policy."

Then, not dismayed, Young Scientist sent his article into the *Proceedings*. Now it happens that Young Scientist had done some work for this magazine before and was quite friendly with some members of the staff, so he encountered no bias here and his article was quickly published. The issue was drawn.

Professor M, now drawn deeper into the debate, wrote an article clearly stating his position and findings. Of course, since he was on the jury of the *Journal*, it was most ethical for him to submit it to the *Proceedings*. There the predictable happened; the article was sent to Young Scientist for review before publication. "Can't our differences be resolved?" asked Young Scientist of Professor M in a private letter. "After all we're supposed to be dealing in facts." Professor M thereupon withdrew the article and sent it to the *Journal*, where it was, of course, published.

This state of affairs continued for a couple of rounds, one periodical taking the material of one side, and the other, the other side. Finally it seemed to Young Scientist that if he ever got into the *Journal,* he would have it made, his case would be won.

This chapter was originally written with correct names and places. Young Scientist kindly agreed to check the manuscript for accuracy. When he returned the rough draft, he asked that this story in its original form be removed. Why? He wrote, "It seems that the *Journal* is going to publish some of our papers before too long." Perhaps I misread his letter, but I seemed to hear a long sigh of wistful anticipation when he mentioned the *Journal.*

The difficulty in publishing blatantly novel ideas is well known. Yet what choice do technical journals really have? To admit unorthodox pieces to their pages, articles at issue with the basic building blocks of their discipline, would, to say the very least, affect circulation. Without prejudgment and selection of articles that fit the paradigms, readers might finally not be able to distinguish between "scientific fact" and dissent, which Dr. McConnell discovered when he published *The Worm Runner's Digest.* This journal, you recall, contained humorous pseudoscientific articles, as well as serious pieces. It was finally necessary to publish the satirical articles upside down so that they could be easily recognized.

Is McConnell's solution the answer? If one can't publish in standard periodicals, should one start a new *Journal?* Obviously such action is not always possible. Not every dissenter can afford his own magazine. Furthermore, separate journals tend to sequester the new concepts rather than disseminate their story to the community which must in the end be their judge and their developer.

Just suppose that major technical journals were to publish one supplemental issue each year in which the articles were not judged by normal standards. The referees, instead of selecting papers on the basis of "scientific merit" (which may simply mean: "fits the paradigm") would select on the basis of maximum possible impact to the discipline. The more important and controversial an idea seems, the more probable its inclusion in this special issue. If the regular referees declined to participate in this kind of selection out of loyalty to their ideals, perhaps a board of special judges could be selected from the loyal opposition.

One senses immediately that this idea cannot succeed in this form. Suppose a reputable scientist were to submit an article to the regular journal, and the editors decided to shuffle it off to the kook issue. Irreparable damage to prestige. In fact, the very selection of the issue in which an article was to appear might become a cold-science weapon. So something has to be added. Suppose that publication in this issue carried with it a cash stipend or a guarantee of research funding. That makes all the difference in the world, if the sum is high enough. Now appearing in this issue might become respectable, maybe even important.

And wouldn't it be fun to read!

If the problem of publication can be answered by special issues that carry honoraria, how about funding, the other major means of denial? How can research be funded fairly when proposals for this work are judged on the basis of "normal" science? As we have seen there are several methods by which worthy research projects derive funds today. Most important is the mission-agency funding where a government agency, in accomplishing the job for which it was created, authorizes certain research projects. Second, the National Science Foundation distributes government funds for projects that relate to basic science, without any visible tie-in to national goals. Third, universities, using their own fiscal resources, can sponsor departmental work. Finally, private foundations and corporations account for an appreciable portion of the investment in the future that today's research represents.

We can assume that the mission oriented agencies are interested in accomplishing their missions and that industry is interested in making profit. Therefore, the research stemming from these sources is most often directed to specific ends: the accomplishment of national goals and the enhancement of our economy (although some of the work funded is only tenuously related to these considerations). If these were the only motivations for research, much of the spontaneity and excitement would be gone from science. Furthermore, in the extreme, science would become constrained and channeled, directed by centralized agencies and private interests. Centralized control would require almost infinitely wise planners, since the ultimate uses of discoveries in the basic sciences are seldom foreseen. Who could have planned in 1870 that the work of James Maxwell in electricity and magnetism would eventually result in our automated society, or that the work of Pierre and Marie Curie in 1900 would be related to techniques used in the investigation of cancer? It is clear that, regardless of the inequities that result from our present techniques for funding "little science," centralized authorization of projects is not the answer.

The National Science Foundation is a "no strings attached" organization. Worthy proposals are granted funds if the review scientists of the Foundation believe the proposed work is well founded. The criteria they employ in reviewing projects includes: the capability of the experimenter, the facilities which he has available to him, the probability of accomplishing the work he has described, and the need and importance of the work. In a nutshell, the proposed work and the experimenter himself must pass the scrutiny of the agency's review scientists; if they believe in him and the validity of his project it may be funded. For projects that follow the paradigms this isn't bad; in fact, in a nation as rich as ours, it would be hard to imagine an investment with more promise. As many scientists have argued, the National Science Foundation can fill in the research gaps that mission-agencies miss; in the limit, this foundation or others like it could provide every qualified and potentially original scientist in the country with funds to pursue the dictates of his expertise.

But what of men who are misjudged and projects that do not fit within the framework of the "possible?" Can we afford to support these as well? Certainly any possible payoff from these marginal situations is less probable. Our present structure has worked well and provided us with the world's pre-eminent technical society. Is there room for more? The history of scientific progress suggests the answer is "yes." After providing for normal scientific expansion, for that portion of research concerned with extending our knowledge in anticipated directions, we should seek a mechanism for supporting the unconventional, the off-beat project, the creative man whose ideas carry him beyond conventional science.

Picture an institution that sponsors odd projects. Perhaps it is a new organization, perhaps it is a special department of an existing foundation. It lives on originality, ingenuity and inspiration. It deals in ideas that do not follow the logical development of the basic science, it deals in practical imagination, in the what-might-be. It deals in concepts of man, his needs and what he wants. It provides a home for wayward ideas and concepts, an ear, a questioning, inquisitive, receptive, perceptive audience for men who think they have something to say. The purpose of the institution would not be to judge but to provide a means for these innovators to try their ideas, to demonstrate their concepts; in effect, to put their accomplishments where their mouths are. There would still be certain criteria to be met. The innovators would be required to show competence in the field of their intended research (high school dropouts need not apply for grants in atomic physics); their intended work should not be trivial (who needs research in better can openers); the institution must not mistake obscurity for profundity. I think these are perhaps the only criteria; certainly missing is the rule that the intended work fit the paradigms of existing science.

There are other steps that could be taken to increase our responsiveness to new concepts. A scientific and technical education now prepares students to believe that which the community has found to be true and excludes competing concepts. This need not be so. It might be valuable to teach a history of science in all advanced curricula, recounting the revolutions in thought, the obstinacy of the community to new ideas, the times when science has been wrong. The cult of phrenology, caloric, phlogiston, Ptolemaic astronomy, all of these were once good science. Fermentation, anaesthesia, asepsis, genetic inheritance, evolution, all of these were once nonscience. Why shouldn't practitioners of science know their heritage and frailty?

Interdisciplinary courses can be taught. Courses in imagination can be designed. For example, Tufts College now teaches a course in inventive design. During one meeting the students are provided a kit of twelve paper clips, one razor blade, six thumbtacks, two safety pins, four pencils, nine rubber bands, two pieces of poster paper, one piece of aluminum foil, four binding pins, and one large envelope. They are asked to construct whatever they can from this agglomerate in six hours. The students of one class produced a record player, an electric motor, a desk calculator, a water pump and a centrifuge. This is technology, not science, but the analogy is clear.

Three social organizations have judged ideas: the Church, government, and science. In the sixteenth century it was the Church, the frenetic ecclesiastics, who judged innovation. Government civil servants now, and increasingly in the future, will control innovation through funding, legislation, and selection of national goals. The time of unbounded science is to come. To a degree all three groups guard their learned dogma and heroic traditions; they protect their mother-beliefs from intrusion; they strive to preserve the underlying status quo. Certain kinds of innovation can become the enemy of status quo, and these ideas suffer in conflict until they die or are finally absorbed into the principles of the judge-group.

When science probes into "acceptable" boxes, its method is efficient. No other social structure has proved so capable of organizing the diverse efforts of men, widely separated in time, geography, and talent, toward the solution of shared problems.

But the method has limits. The bounds of its problems are finite; its rejection of good ideas and talented men proves its fallibility. Cranks and legitimate players who deviate from the game-rules are treated harshly and indiscriminately.

Should the method be annulled in the interests of innovation? Probably not. Science, freed from the confining framework which directs its applications, would be boundless but chaotic. In chaos, progress would be random and regression probable. Instead the method needs receptivity, an ear for the best ideas men can offer, and this requires, ultimately, in science as well as in the Church and government, a sensitivity to man himself.

# NOTES

CHAPTER 1

p. 9  Material relating to Thalidomide drawn from Helen B. Taussig, "The Thalidomide Syndrome," *Scientific American*, August 1962, p. 29.

p. 10  Laurence J. Lafleur, "Cranks and Scientists," *The Scientific Monthly*, November 1951, pp. 284–291.

p. 12  John Tyndall, *Advancement of Science*, K. Butts Company, New York, 1874, p. 38.

p. 15  Public opinion survey from *Los Angeles Times*, The Harris Survey, November 1, 1965, p. 14. 45% for, 42% against, 13% undecided. If the Russians were not in space: 38% for, 50% against, 12% undecided.

p. 15  Scientists and engineers statistic: Neil P. Ruzic, *The Case for Going to the Moon*, G. P. Putnam's Sons, New York, 1965, p. 4. 18% for, 16% against, 65% undecided.

p. 15  Research expenditure estimates from Basic Research & National Goals, A Report to the Committee on Science & Astronautics, U. S. House of Representatives, March 1965, p. 310.


CHAPTER 2

p. 20  Immanuel Velikovsky, *Worlds in Collision*, pp. 71 and 115, Copyright 1950 by Immanuel Velikovsky, reprinted by permission of Doubleday & Company, Inc., New York.

p. 20    Story about Conquistadores, *ibid.*, p. 73, quoting De Landa, *Yucatan*, **p. 8.**

p. 20    *Ibid.*, p. 74, words of Lapland God.

p. 21    Mexican tale from Zelia Nuttel, *The Fundamental Principles of Old and New World Civilizations*, p. 707, Harvard University Peabody Museum, Cambridge, Massachusetts, 1901.

p. 23    Summary of unusual predictions from *Worlds in Collision* and Immanuel Velikovsky, "Some Aditional Examples of Correct Prognosis," *The American Behavioral Scientist,* September 1963, pp. 50–54.

p. 23    *The New York Times,* April 2, 1950, reviewer: Walkemar Kaempffert.

p. 26    Lafleur, *op. cit.*, p. 287.

p. 28    Warren Guthrie, "Books, Civilization, and Science," *Science,* April 20, 1951, p. 429.

p. 31    Atwater letter and editor's reply from Alred de Grazia, Ralph E. Juergens, Livio G. Strecchini, *The Politics of Science,* Metron, Inc., New York, 1963, p. 57.

p. 33    Quotation about Catholic Church from Livio C. Strecchini, "The Inconsistent Heavens," *The American Behavioral Scientist,* September 1963, p. 28.

p. 35    This book planned by Velikovsky on Freud and his heroes was set aside, but a portion of its subject matter was developed in Dr. Velikovsky's book *Oedipus and Akhnaton,* published in 1960. Here, Akhnaton was identified as an historical antecedent of Oedipus.

p. 35    Reference to Venus in later Mexican and Hebrew documents from Velikovsky, *op. cit.*, p. 161.

p. 35    Reference to Incas' name for Venus from William H. Prescott, *The Conquest of Peru,* Dolphin Books, Garden City, New York, pp. 68 and 87.

p. 35    Sacrifices made to Venus, from James G. Frazer, *The Golden Bough,* The Macmillan Company, New York, 1958, p. 501.

p. 36    Surface temperature of Venus dropping, from address at Temple University, March 23, 1966.

p. 37    Direction of Venus' rotation from Cornell H. Mayer, Radio-astronomy Studies of Venus and Mars, *Astronautics and Aeronautics,* April 1966.

p. 37    Resonant orbit, from *The New York Times,* April 23, 1966.

p. 38    F. Hoyle, *Frontiers of Astronomy,* New York, Harper & Row, 1955, pp. 68–72.

p. 38    NASA Report, *Mariner Mission to Venus,* p. 111.

p. 39    Charles MacKay, *Extraordinary Popular Delusions,* published by Richard Bentley, 1841, republished by L. C. Page Company, 1932, p. 258.

p. 40    Reference to length of comets from Fletcher G. Watson, *Between the Planets,* Harvard University Press, 1956, p. 58.

p. 40    Reference to the weight of the 1770 comet, *ibid.*, p. 64.

p. 41    Reference to N. T. Bobrovnikoff's estimate from Watson, *op. cit.*, p. 66 and Moore, *op. cit.*, pp. 68–71.

p. 43    Reference to oceanographers' findings from Velikovsky, *op. cit., Some Additional Examples.*

p. 43    Velikovsky, *Earth in Upheaval,* Doubleday & Company, Inc., Garden City, New York, 1955.

p. 44    Gerald S. Hawkins, *Stonehenge Decoded,* Doubleday & Company, Garden City, New York, 1965.

p. 45    Dating tests, from R. J. C. Atkinson, *Stonehenge,* Hamish Hamilton, London, 1956.

p. 46    Lafleur, *op. cit.*, p. 288.

p. 46    Flies vs. Venus' heat argument from Donald Menzel, "The Debate Over Velikovsky," *Harper's,* December 1963, p. 83.

CHAPTER 3

p. 60    Quotation relating to Bennett's answer from *The Worm Runner's Digest,* J. McConnell, Editor, University of Michigan, Mental Health Research Institute, Ann Arbor, Michigan, Volume VII, No. 1, p. 6.

p. 62    Plant training article, Eric Holmes and Gail Gruenberg; "Learning in Plants?", *The Worm Runner's Digest,* April 1965, pp. 9–10.

p. 64    "Joke" magazine quote from James V. McConnell, ed., *The Worm Re-Turns,* Prentice-Hall, Inc., Englewood Cliffs, New Jersey, 1965, p. xi.

p. 64    "Scientific publication" quote from *ibid.*, p. x.

p. 69    For a more complete discussion of this RNA theory see: James V. McConnell, "The Modern Search for the Engram," from *A Manuel of Psychological Experimentation on Planarians,* a special publication of *The Worm Runner's Digest,* University of Michigan, Mental Health Research Institute, Ann Arbor, Michigan, 1965, pp. 1–9.

p. 69    For Wilder's experiments see: Wilder Penfield & Lamar Roberts, *Speech and Brain Mechanisms,* Princeton University Press, New Jersey, 1959.

CHAPTER 4

p. 72    California Datura weed use by teenagers from Associated Press, September 16, 1965.

p. 75    J. S. Slotkin, "Menomini Peyotism," *Transactions of the American Philosophical Society,* 1952, Vol. 42, Part 4, pp. 568–570.

p. 77    Aldous Huxley, *The Doors of Perception,* Harper & Row, New York, 1954, pp. 17, 19, 26 and 53.

p. 79    Subject's reaction to LSD from John Kobler, "The Dangerous Magic of LSD," *The Saturday Evening Post,* November 2, 1963, p. 32.

p. 80    LSD made at home, from Richard Blum *et al., Utopiates,* Atherton Press, New York, 1964, p. 38.

p. 80    Orgiastic excitement a feature of LSD, *ibid.,* p. 32.

p. 81    Timothy Leary, *Interpersonal Diagnosis of Personality,* Ronald Press, New York, 1957.

p. 83    Leary's introduction to mushrooms from *The Problems of Expanding Consciousness,* Radio Interview between Timothy Leary and Fred Haines, KPFK-FM, Los Angeles, April 1963.

p. 83    Leary's drug experience quoted from Kobler, *op. cit.,* p. 31.

p. 83    Cutting through game structure of Western life from an unpublished lecture, "How to Change Behavior," Dr. Timothy Leary, p. 6.

p. 85    Reactions of subjects to LSD, *ibid.,* p. 9.

p. 86    Reaction of prisoners to LSD therapy, *op. cit.,* KPFK-FM Radio Interview, and *op. cit.,* Leary Lecture, pp. 10–11.

p. 87    Eviction story, KPFK-FM Interview, *op.cit.*

p. 87    Dangerous drug quote from *Time,* March 29, 1963, p. 72.

p. 88    Joseph J. Downing, "Zihuatenejo: An Experiment in Transpersonative Living," a chapter in *Utopiates,* by Richard Blum *et al.,* Atherton Press, New York, 1964.

p. 89    *Ibid.,* p. 162.

p. 90    *Ibid.,* p. 163.

p. 91    Timothy Leary, Ph.D., Ralph Metzner, Ph.D., and Richard Alpert, Ph.D., *The Psychedelic Experience,* University Books, New Hyde Park, New York, 1964, p. 137.

p. 94    Pleasure of LSD experience, KPFK-FM Interview, *op. cit.*

p. 95    Quotation drawing analogy between society's response to LSD and automobiles from Timothy Leary, Richard Alpert, "The Politics of Consciousness Expansion," *The Harvard Review,* Summer 1963, pp. 36–37.

p. 95    KPFK-FM Interview, *op. cit.*

CHAPTER 5

p. 97    Number of carbonaceous chondrites found, from Harold C. Urey, *A Review of Evidence for Biological Material in Meteorites,* a paper presented at COSPAR meeting, May 1965, p. 1.

p. 97  First observed fall from Walter Sullivan, *We Are Not Alone,* McGraw-Hill Book Company, New York, 1964, p. 104.

p. 98  Berzelius' question from J. J. Berzelius, *Ann. Phys. Chem.* 33, 113 (1834), quoted by Urey, *op. cit.,* p. 1.

p. 100  B. Nagy, W. G. Menschein, and D. J. Hennessy, "Mass Spectrographic Analysis of the Orgueil Meteorite," *Annals of the New York Academy of Sciences,* 1961, 93:25.

p. 100  *The New York Times,* March 17, 1961.

p. 101  Dr. Nagy's quote from an article by David Bergamini, "Wax and Wigglers: Life in Space?" *Life,* May 5, 1961, p. 59.

p. 103  Quotation relating to morphology from Edward Anders and Frank Fitch, "Organized Element: Possible Identification in Orgueil Meteorite," *Science,* June 7, 1963, p. 1099.

p. 103  View that the shapes may have been produced by inorganic process, from Frank Fitch, Henry P. Schwartz, and Edward Anders, "Organized Elements in Carbonaceous Chondrites," *Nature,* March 24, 1962, pp. 1124–1125.

p. 103  Quote from Professor Anders, from *Proceedings of Lunar and Planetary Exploration Colloquium,* held at North American Aviation, May 23 and 24, 1961, Vol. 11, No. 4, 15 November 1961, p. 63.

p. 103  Description of dialogue, from Robert O'Brien, "Somebody Up There Likes Us," *Esquire,* December 1963, p. 187.

p. 104  Dr. H. C. Urey, in a panel discussion at the New York Academy of Sciences. Quoted by O'Brien, *op. cit.,* p. 232.

p. 108  Back-contamination quotation from *A Review of Space Research,* Academy Research Council publication no. 1079, National Academy of Sciences, National Research Council (1962), Washington, D.C., pp. 9–13.

p. 109  Moon origin hypothesis, Dr. H. C. Urey, "Life Forms in Meteorites," *Nature,* March 24, 1962, pp. 1120–1121.

p. 109  Subsurface glaciers on the moon, from Zdenek Kopal, *Internal Structure of the Moon, Technology of Lunar Exploration,* C. I. Cummings and H. R. Lawrence, eds., Academic Press, New York, 1963.

p. 110  Mars vegetation, from *Vestnik Akademii SSSR (U.S.S.R. Academy of Sciences Journal),* No. 10, October 1962. Translated in *Space Intelligence Notes,* George C. Marshall Space Flight Center, Huntsville, Alabama, August 1963, p. 20.

p. 110  Reproduction of organisms in Mars atmosphere, from J. Kooistra, Jr., R. B. Mitchell, and H. Strungheld, *The Behavior of Microorganisms Under Simulated Martian Conditions,* Publications of the Astronautical Society of the Pacific, Vol. 70, 1958, p. 64.

p. 111  Brian Mason, "Organic Matter from Space," *Scientific American,* March 1963, p. 49.

p. 113  Sterilization of meteorite, *op. cit., Proceedings of Lunar and Planetary Exploration Colloquium,* p. 68.

p. 114   Samples looking like sausages, from John A. Osmundsen, *The New York Times,* April 6, 1961, p. 37.

p. 114   Resembling size and shape of bacteria, from "Scientists Find Life Far Out," *Medical World News,* January 19, 1962, p. 26.

p. 114   A helix cut into small pieces, *op. cit., Proceedings of Lunar and Planetary Exploration Colloquium,* p. 69.

p. 115   Generation of rod-like particles, *Ibid.,* p. 69.


CHAPTER 6

p. 122   Number of societies and their distances, from Frank D. Drake, *The Radio Search for Intelligent Extraterrestrial Life,* a paper delivered at a symposium on exobiology at the Jet Propulsion Laboratory, Pasadena, California. Many observations of this chapter are drawn from that paper.

p. 126   For an account of this exchange between Doctors Cocconi and Lovell: *op. cit.,* Sullivan, *We Are Not Alone,* p. 191.

p. 127   Otto Struve, "Astronomers in Turmoil," *Physics Today,* September 1960, p. 22.

p. 128   Quotation about Ozma funding and limitations from a personal correspondence with Dr. Drake, September 21, 1965.

p. 131   Elder statesmen in radioastronomy from Shirley Thomas quoting Frank Drake, *Men of Space,* Vol. 6, Chilton Books, Philadelphia and New York, 1963, p. 75.

p. 131   Freeman Dyson, *Science,* "Search for Artificial Stellar Sources of Infrared Radiation," Vol. 131, 1960, p. 1667.

p. 132   Russian concept of advanced civilizations from *Time,* November 6, 1964, p. 38.

p. 133   *Tass* interview from *The New York Times,* April 13, 1965, p. 1.

p. 134   Professor Shklovsky quoted, from *Los Angeles Times,* April 14, 1965, p. 3, and *The New York Times,* April 14, 1965, p. 3.

p. 135   Reporter's question, *op. cit., Los Angeles Times,* April 14, 1965, p. 3.

p. 136   Kardashev quote, *Ibid.*

p. 138   Round-trip journey statistics, from Sebastian von Hoerner, "The General Limits of Space Travel," *Science,* July 6, 1962, pp. 18–23.

p. 139   Reference to anti-gravity possibilities from Theodore J. Gordon, *The Future,* St. Martin's Press, New York, 1965, p. 69.

p. 140   Anti-gravity forecast from Olaf Helmer and T. J. Gordon, *Report on a Long Range Forecasting Study,* Rand P-2982, 1964.

p. 141   Geoffrey Burbidge and Fred Hoyle, "Anti-Matter," *Scientific American,* April 1958.

p. 142 "Towards Flight Without Stress or Strain . . . or Weight," *Inter-Avia*, Vol. XI, No. 5.

p. 142 Anomalies in the motions of pendulums, see Maurice F. C. Allais, "Should the Laws of Gravitation Be Reconsidered?" *Aero/Space Engineering*, October 1959, p. 51.

p. 143 *New World Translation of the Holy Scriptures*, International Bible Students Association, Brooklyn, New York, p. 917.

p. 145 Shklovsky's hypothesis, *op. cit.*, Walter Sullivan, *We Are Not Alone*, p. 166.

CHAPTER 7

p. 147 Reverend Franklin Loehr, *The Power of Prayer on Plants*, Doubleday & Company, Inc., Garden City, New York, 1959.

p. 148 *Ibid.*, pp. 46-47.

p. 148 *Ibid.*, p. 50.

p. 150 Reference to the Stella C. experiment is made by Dr. J. B Rhine in *The Reach of the Mind*, William Sloane Associates, New York, 1947, p. 91.

p. 152 Reverend Loehr quotation about the Princeton symposium from personal correspondence, June 30, 1965.

p. 156 Robert Hatch, *Nation*, May 2, 1959.

p. 156 Quotation from a private correspondence with Reverend Loehr, June 30, 1065.

p. 157 Quotation relating to "in-tune" phenomena from J. C. Lilly, *Man and Dolphin*, Doubleday & Company, Inc., Garden City, New York, 1961, p. 207.

CHAPTER 8

p. 162 Quotation relating to experiment odds from *op. cit.* Rhine, *Reach of the Mind*, p. 35.

p. 163 Biographies of Edgar Cayce: Thomas Sugrue, *There Is a River*, Henry Holt & Company, New York, 1942. And Gina Cerminara, *Many Mansions*, William Morrow & Company, New York, 1950.

p. 164 Reference to Cayce's accuracy, *op. cit.*, Cerminara, p. 19.

p. 165 Quotation about Selma, Alabama girl, *op. cit.*, Cerminara, p. 12.

p. 167 Quotation about Cayce and Rhine from Jess Stearn, *The Door to the Future*, Doubleday & Company, Inc., Garden City, New York, 1963, p. 68.

p. 171   Quotation about prophecy, *op. cit.*, J. B. Rhine, p. 68.

p. 173   Lincoln quotation from Carl Sandburg, *Abraham Lincoln, The War Years*, Dell Publishing Company, New York, pp. 825–826.

p. 175   Translation of the quatrains from Charles A. Ward, *Oracles of Nostradamus*, Charles Scribner's Sons, New York, 1940.

p. 179   Probability quotation from *op. cit.*, Dr. Rhine, p. 70.

p. 180   Salesman story from George H. Estabrooks and Nancy E. Gross, *The Future of the Human Mind*, E. P. Dutton and Company, New York, 1961, p. 200.

p. 184   Quotation relating to ESP criticism from J. B. Rhine and Associates, *Parapsychology from Duke to FRNM*, the Parapsychology Press, Durham, North Carolina, 1965, p. 14. The history of ESP Research in the United States is largely drawn from this source as well.

p. 185   American Psychological Association reference from *Ibid.*, p. 27.

p. 191   Rand Corporation study, *op. cit.*, T. J. Gordon and Olaf Helmer, p. 35.

CHAPTER 9

p. 196   R. C. W. Ettinger, *The Prospect of Immortality*, Doubleday & Company, Inc., Garden City, New York, 1964.

p. 197   The history of the book, *The Prospect of Immortality*, and the biographical material as well, is drawn from personal correspondence from Mr. Ettinger, dated December 18, 1965 and December 20, 1965.

p. 197   R. C. W. Ettinger, "Lasting Indefinitely," *Esquire*, May 1965, p. 136. Contains statement about lack of scientific errors.

p. 198   Review of *The Prospect of Immortality* from *Science*, July 31, 1964, p. 475.

p. 198   Ruzic's critique from *op. cit.*, Neil P. Ruzic, p. 216.

p. 198   Rand study, *op. cit.*, Olaf Helmer and T. J. Gordon.

p. 199   R. E. Lapp reference from Albert Rosenfeld, "Will Man Direct His Own Evolution," *Life*, October 1, 1965, p. 102.

p. 199   Frozen rabbit ova, *ibid.*

p. 199   Freezing experimentation progress, from private correspondence of R. C. W. Ettinger, December 18, 1965.

p. 200   Reports of freezing experiments from *op. cit.*, Ettinger, *The Prospect of Immortality*, pp. 11–15 and 49.

p. 201   Thawing method examples from *op. cit.*, Ettinger, *The Prospect of Immortality*.

p. 202   Time payment quote from Hugh McPherson, "Man Tries to Deepfreeze Wife's Corpse," *The National Enquirer*, August 15, 1965, p. 7.

p. 202 "Universal esteem" quote from *op. cit.* Ettinger, "Lasting Indefinitely," p. 142.

p. 203 UPI release in the *Los Angeles Times,* May 21, 1965.

p. 204 Husband's quote from *op. cit.,* McPherson.

p. 204 Reverend K. M. Glaesner, "The Prospect of Immortality," a sermon delivered at the St. John's Evangelical Lutheran Church, Springfield, Ohio, June 12, 1965.

p. 205 "To each his own" quote from *op. cit.,* Ettinger, "Lasting Indefinitely."

CHAPTER 10

p. 209 Amalgam story and quote from M. D. K. Bremner, *The Story of Dentistry,* Dental Items of Interest Publishing Company, Brooklyn, New York, 1958, pp. 151–153.

p. 210 Pledge from *Ibid.*

p. 214 Theory differences, material drawn from Albert Schatz and Joseph Martin, "What Caries Research Offers the Graduating Dentist," *The New York State Dental Journal,* March 1961, pp. 127–132.

p. 216 Quote regarding American journals' refusal to publish paper, *op. cit.,* Schatz and Martin, "What Caries Research Offers."

p. 216 Incompetence quote from Schatz and Martin, *Some Historical Aspects of Caries Research,* a paper presented to the Symposium on Dental Caries, University of Concepción, Concepción, Chile, July 1963.

p. 217 Suspended judgment quote from *Journal of American Dental Association,* 65:375, 1962.

p. 218 From private correspondence, December 15, 1965.

p. 218 Quoted material relating to *The Toxicology of Flourine* appeared in a review in the *Pakistan Dental Journal,* 15:68–71, 1965.

p. 220 Fluorine censorship quote from *Prevention,* June 1965.

p. 222 Bernard Forscher and Hamilton Robinson, letter to the editor, *Dental Times,* June 15, 1961.

p. 223 Personal correspondence from Dr. Schatz, December 15, 1965.

p. 224 Survey of opinion about chelation from Charles F. Bodecker, "Consultant Evaluation on the Proteolysis-Chelation Theory of Dental Caries," *The New York State Dental Journal,* October 22, 1956.

CHAPTER 11

p. 228  Number of scientists and cost of projects from George B. Kistiakowsky, *On Federal Support of Basic Research, Basic Research and National Goals,* a Report to the Committee on Science and Astronautics, United States House of Representatives, March 1965.

p. 228  Source of funds, *ibid.,* Appendix A, p. 312.

p. 234  Decentralization of basic research, *ibid.*

p. 236  D. S. Greenberg, "The 200 BEV Machine: University Compact Offers Its Services," *Science,* December 17, 1965, p. 1567.

p. 238  *U. S. Foreign Policy and the Soviet Union,* Fred Warner Neal, Center for the Study of Democratic Institutions, Santa Barbara, California, 1961, p. 59.

p. 241  Description of Soviet academics drawn from "Research Administration and the Administrator: U.S.S.R. and U.S.," Norman Kaplan, *Administrative Science Quarterly,* Vol. 6, 1961, pp. 51–72.

p. 242  Quotation from a speech by Nieh Jung-chen, Chairman of the Planning Committee for the Development of Science, New China News Agency, Shanghai, January 15, 1959.

p. 242  Twelve year scientific program quote, *ibid.,* p. 60.

CHAPTER 12

p. 245  Thomas S. Kuhn, *The Structure of Scientific Revolutions,* University of Chicago Press, Chicago, Illinois, 1962.

p. 253  Quotation from S. Pasternack, Editor, *Physical Review Letters,* February 1, 1960, pp. 109–110.

p. 253  Quotation from S. A. Goudsmit, Editor, *Physical Review Letters,* January 1, 1960, pp. 1–2.

p. 257  In 1961–62, the federal government provided about 57% of the expenditure in basic research in the United States, industry 24%, colleges and universities 12%, and other nonprofit institutions 7%. Within this government sector, the Department of Defense, NASA, the Atomic Energy Commission, and the Department of Health, Education and Welfare accounted for most of the expenditures. (*Op. cit. Basic Research.*)

p. 260  Tufts College course material from Percy H. Hill, *Techniques of Instruction in Inventive Design,* a paper presented at a symposium of the American Society of Mechanical Engineers, Chicago, Illinois, November 7–11, 1965.